Legends of Sacrifice, Nobility and Lust

From the mist-shrouded world of the Norsemen come these marvelous tales of adventure, vibrant with life and imagination.

It is the world of myth . . . of an awesome race of Goth kings, fierce, cunning, proud, who were descended from the god Odin. It is a world of legend . . . of men and women become larger than life through the gift of unknown poets. It is a world of magic and incantations, of inviolable oaths and blood-vengeance, of exalted doom and sublime death.

Here, in the magnificent translation by the outstanding nineteenth-century poet, are the stories which form the great common literary heritage of the Scandinavians, the British and the Germans. The stories pulsate in the Wagnerian spectacle; they sing in a great poem by Morris; they echo in the plays of Ibsen.

Skillfully and with impressive mastery, Robert W. Gutman provides an excellent introduction in which he traces the origins of the Volsunga Saga, its significance, its development, its variations, its impact on nineteenth-century culture and its reverberations in twentieth-century politics.

Mr. Gutman, presently on the faculty of the University of the State of New York, has taugh art history and design at the College of the City of New York and the New School for Social Research. He is a founder and a director of the Master Classes at the Bayreuth Festival in Germany where he lectures on Wagner and his works.

Translated by

WILLIAM MORRIS

VOLSUNGA

SAGA

The Story of the
Volsungs and Niblungs

With an Introduction and Glossary

by ROBERT W. GUTMAN

COLLIER BOOKS
NEW YORK, N.Y.

Collier Books is a division of The Crowell-Collier Publishing
Company

First Collier Books Edition 1962

Contents

SONGS FROM THE ELDER EDDA.

Introduction

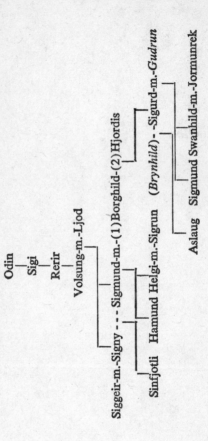

THE VOLSUNG LINE

Odin
Sigi
Rerir
Volsung-m.-Ljod

Siggeir-m.-Signy - - - Sigmund-m.-(1) Borghild-(2) Hjordis

Sinfjotli   Hamund   Helgi-m.-Sigrun   (Brynhild) - -Sigurd-m.-Gudrun

Aslaug   Sigmund   Swanhild-m.-Jormunrek

THE LINE OF BUDLI

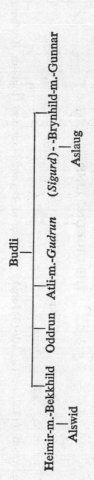

Heimir-m.-Bekkhild   Oddrun   Atli-m.-*Gudrun*   (*Sigurd*) - Brynhild-m.-Gunnar
    |
  Alswid   Aslaug

Budli

THE GIUKUNG LINE

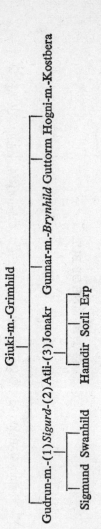

Giuki-m.-Grimhild

Gudrun-m.-(1)*Sigurd*-(2)Atli-(3)Jonakr   Gunnar-m.-*Brynhild* Guttorm Hogni-m.-Kostbera

Sigmund Swanhild   Hamdir Sorli Erp

Introduction to the Volsunga Saga

1

THE CHARACTERS and dramatic situations in the *Volsunga Saga,* here presented in William Morris' superb translation, will be familiar even to those who are reading it for the first time. The Volsung, Sigmund, who pulls an enchanted sword from an oak where it had been placed for him by a one-eyed god; the valkyrie, Brynhild, awakened on her fire-girt mountain by Sigmund's son; the cunning Rhenish draughts that destroy the memory—such magic situations are already part of the theatrical experience of three generations through the tetralogy, *The Nibelung's Ring,* of Richard Wagner. Thus his name will pervade the following introduction much as a leading motif weaves its way through one of his scores. His is the version of the Sigurd story that the world knows best, and the *Volsunga Saga* was one of its principal sources.

The purpose of this introduction is to discuss the *Volsunga Saga* and its origins, to compare it with the *Nibelungenlied,* a contemporaneous German treatment of the same material, and then to bring both into relationship with the mighty work they nourished, Wagner's *The Nibelung's Ring,* certainly one of the capstones of a great century's art.

It is hoped that the tremendous vitality of the legend will be demonstrated; arising in the mists of unrecorded history, its astonishing longevity is shown by the fact that Wagner's cycle to this day must be performed at least every few years by any lyric theatre that pretends to eminence. The raging flames and rising floods conceived ages ago by the Teutonic poets have become through Wagner's work the problems of today's scenic designers and technicians. And the Nibelungen operas have left their mark not only on staging and theatre design; but, of course, on music and drama as a whole. They have, alas, affected even politics, for an unhealthy age turned Sigurd, the god of light, into a symbol of doom and darkness, a transformation which, it will be observed, Wagner prepared by his particular juxtaposition of various Norse tales.

Henrik Ibsen's splendid early play, *The Vikings at Helgeland,* which owes much to the *Volsunga Saga,* will be touched upon. Finally William Morris' *Sigurd,* a poem described by George Bernard Shaw as the greatest epic since Homer, will be discussed to show how an Englishman of genius, contemporary with Wagner, reacted to the Teutonic heritage represented by the *Volsunga Saga.*

2

This book reprints the most fascinating family history and adventure tale of Norse mythology. Its range of emotion and tragic force make it one of the landmarks of world literature, and William Morris' translation is the work of a man who keenly felt and responded to its power and vigor.

The Eddic and saga tales are the great common literary legacy of the Teutonic peoples—the Scandinavians, the British, and the Germans. In *Beowulf* (*ca.* 675-725), the most important example of Anglo-Saxon verse and the first piece to be considered in most chronological studies of English literature, a version of the *Volsunga Saga* is retold. After Beowulf's victory over the monster, a chieftain whose mind is filled with old legends compliments the hero with a poem comparing Beowulf's deeds with those of the greatest of Germanic heroes, "Sigmund the son of Volsung." Thus in a work that is the oldest surviving epic of any Teutonic people, the Volsung story commands attention for its fame and venerableness.

It is recorded that the famous Icelandic poet, Egil Skallagrimsson (*ca.* 900–980), shipwrecked off the Northumbrian coast, was captured and taken before his ancient enemy, Eric

Blood-Axe, who held sway at York (*ca.* 936). Egil had dedicated a pole of magic runes in Norway to the destruction of Eric, and had slain one of his sons. Yet Egil was given his freedom after he had performed a Norse panegyric to the king. That highly were the poems of the "dönsk tunga" valued in ancient Yorkshire, and so esteemed were the skalds who composed them. It is possible that sagas were still chanted in England up to the time of the Conquest. However, England's cultural life then became tied to Western Europe, and its links with the Northern lands loosened; for centuries the heroic tales of the Eddas and sagas were forgotten.

During the eighteenth century, English writers began to show interest in their almost lost Norse heritage, and Thomas Gray, who had some knowledge of Icelandic, produced his *The Descent of Odin* and *The Fatal Sisters*.

The nineteenth century saw a real vogue for the saga tales, and the English William Morris and the German Richard Wagner represent the most important resurgence of the Eddic material and spirit. Ibsen's *The Vikings at Helgeland* was also a powerful contribution to this literature. Notwithstanding its subject, Matthew Arnold's *Balder Dead* has a classical rather than a Norse aesthetic, and Christian Hebbel's great trilogy, *Die Nibelungen,* is only indirectly related since he drew his material from a medieval German source that reflects the northern tradition.

Before turning to the work of Morris and Wagner in this field, we must consider the Norse and German material of which they both availed themselves. Morris' relationship to it was twofold: At first he appears as a translator, anxious to render faithfully its meaning and spirit; then, later in life, like Wagner, he let his creative powers play over the tales, and from them he embroidered his lyric poem, *Sigurd*. Thus both men, in the course of their careers, reshaped the fabric of the Eddas and sagas into personal creations.

To appreciate both their debt to the legends and their transformation of them, a consideration of the Eddas and sagas is necessary to discover what they were and when they came into being. There are extant three Icelandic sources and one German source which concern this discussion. The former include two Eddas and one saga—the *Elder* or *Poetic Edda,* the *Younger* or *Prose Edda*, and the *Volsunga Saga;* the latter is the *Nibelungenlied.*

It must be remarked before proceeding that no one really knows what the word "Edda" means, but of the various suggestions put forward it is most profitable to accept a definition relating it to poetics.

In the second half of the ninth century, Norwegians, fleeing the authority of King Harald, reached out into the sea to colonize Iceland and later Greenland. Settlements were also established in the Western Isles, that is, England, Scotland, and Ireland. The *Elder Edda* (or Poetic Edda) is a heterogeneous collection of lays created by anonymous poets of Norwegian stock partly in Norway, perhaps as early as the seventh century; in the tenth and eleventh centuries the remaining poems took form in districts on the Atlantic Islands peopled by the wanderers from the mainland.

There is much disagreement concerning the exact provenance and dates of these poems. Some believe that most of the *Edda* was originally created in the British Isles by the Norse settlers and that the poems represent an amalgamation of Norse and Celtic traditions; others hold that Iceland is the home of most of the poems. However, since Iceland itself was settled not only by the Norwegians but also by people from the Hebrides and Ireland, this, too, might account for the Celtic drama in the best of the lays.

Whatever its ultimate origin, most significantly for us, the *Elder Edda* contains a series of poems (beginning with the *Lays of Helgi Hundingsbane* and ending with the *Lay of Hamdir*) that relates most of the great scenes of the Volsung and Nibelung tragedy. Whoever composed the collection (and it was not until about 1200 that the lays were put into writing in Iceland) felt it necessary to fill by prose insertions the gaps in the poems that oral tradition had transmitted in a less than complete state. The *Edda* was fashioned from the common stuff of German, Norse, Anglo-Saxon, and Celtic legends. It is made up of over thirty separate pieces and falls rather neatly into two almost equal sections—one devoted to the tales of the gods, the other of the heroes.

Although the authors of the poems were all of Norwegian

background, the heroes they celebrate are mainly those of the Teutonic heroic age, the era of the migrations of the Germanic tribes, the Goths, the Huns, and the Burgundians. For centuries they had pressed against the ever weakening Rhine-Danube frontier of the western Empire. It now gave way as they marched into Imperial territory and carved it into petty kingdoms. At the same time, the Jutes, Angles, and Saxons, related Teutonic peoples who inhabited Jutland and the plain beyond the frontier, set sail for the great Western Isle left undefended by the contracting might of Rome. But for all the Germanic folk it was the exploits of those who crossed the Rhine that furnished the most cherished stock of material whenever tales of courage and daring were to be told.

Their deeds were certainly first extolled in verse and song in their own Gothic, Burgundian, Lombard, and Frankish lands during the fifth and sixth centuries. Of these nothing has survived. But over the centuries the tales passed, certainly not without modification, into the traditions of other Teutonic peoples and other Teutonic tongues. The *Elder Edda* has preserved them for us and can really be called the *Iliad* of the North. The Norsemen of the Middle Ages looked back upon Sigmund and Sigurd much as Hellenistic Greeks looked upon Priam and Hector.

The heroic adventures of the Rhine interested a tremendous area that extended from Greenland to the Black Sea. It must be remembered that between the eighth and thirteenth centuries, the language of the Norsemen in many variants and dialects was carried to a large part of Europe from the Scandinavian penninsulas—to much of England, Scotland, Ireland, parts of France, and the lower and eastern shores of the Baltic Sea right down to the Swedish kingdom, whose center was the great city of Kiev. In Byzantium it was the language of the Emperor's bodyguard. Indeed, it was the first European tongue spoken in the Western hemisphere.

The Norse, who in the eighth century started their ravaging raids upon Europe's coastal realms, later actually occupied lands and established kingdoms of their own. Runic inscriptions and carvings attest to their widespread travels and influence, and the Eddic stories form the repertory of this art. Though, as far as we know, it was first committed to writing fairly late, the substance of the *Elder Edda* was carried by oral tradition halfway round the world. When this tradition eventually spent itself, fate—a word so important in Northern literature—guarded the abused vellum sheets upon which the *Elder Edda* was preserved until the seventeenth century, when they were rediscovered in an Icelandic farmhouse.

The *Prose Edda* (or Younger Edda) is a manual for poets written in part by Snorri Sturluson (*ca.* 1179–1241), a famous literary figure and politician of Iceland, on his maternal side a descendant of that Egil Skallagrimsson whose panegyric had pacified King Eric. It is based to a great extent upon the poems of the *Elder Edda*, which it rearranges and interprets, and contains a brisk rehearsal of the Volsung story, which begins like Wagner's *The Nibelung's Ring* with the events leading to the theft of the gold and the curse upon it.

In addition to the two Eddas there are various prose sagas, poetic tales, histories, and romances which can be assigned dates ranging from the sixth to the fourteenth centuries. These occasionally deal with material cognate with the Eddas; one in particular is the substance of this book.

About half a century after Snorri set down his *Prose Edda*, an anonymous author in Iceland wrote the *Volsunga Saga*, another re-creation in prose of the series of Volsung poems in the *Elder Edda* but more detailed and elaborate than Snorri's nimble account. In high Gothic times the creator of the *Volsunga Saga*, perhaps under Snorri's influence, was nostalgically looking back upon the glories of his race's Golden Age on the Rhine. Certainly a copy of the *Elder Edda* lay before him as he wrote, and, like the one that Snorri used to compile his *Prose Edda*, it was a version more complete than the mutilated copy that has endured to our day with missing pages and indecipherable words.

Thus the *Volsunga Saga* fills gaps in the surviving Volsung poems of the *Elder Edda* and connects these great poetic scenes and dialogues (here reduced to prose) with a swift narrative that is artistically convincing if not always logically consistent. These matters will be discussed in detail somewhat later, for it is from this thirteenth century Icelandic source, preserving the loftiness of its Eddic origins, that Morris made his translation.

To these Icelandic sources must be added a medieval German or, more properly Austrian redaction of the Norse legends concerning the Volsungs and Nibelungs, the *Nibelungenlied*. Actually it is contemporary with the *Volsunga Saga;* but while the Icelandic version mirrors the character of the primeval Edda, the spirit of the *Nibelungenlied* is quite different. Here the heroic tales have undergone radical transmogrification, and the rough Teutonic heroes now exhibit the knightly ways of the Minnesinger.

The gentle Rudeger of Bechlaren in the *Nibelungenlied*, bound by inviolable pledges to both sides of the conflict, laments that he must fight against his friends, and despite his dilemma finds an honorable death. He is a type who could hardly have existed in the old sagas. Yet, in this amazing poem primitive elements suddenly rise and trouble its chivalric surface; recognizable historical figures such as Theodoric the Ostrogoth (Dietrich of Bern) move in a world still haunted by the mysterious red gold of the Nibelung hoard, the magic sword, and the miraculous cloud-cloak called the *tarnkappe*. Dragons, giants, and mermaids still lurk beyond the medieval town walls.

Although Wagner formed *The Nibelung's Ring* mainly from the Norse sources, it was to the *Nibelungenlied* that he turned to extract and develop the mighty figure of Hagen; similarly the forest scene in *The Twilight of the Gods* rests upon the marvelous presentation in the German epic of Siegfried's death at the spring. William Morris also introduces into his *Sigurd*, a poem quite faithful to the *Volsunga Saga*, ideas suggested by the powerful *Nibelungenlied*. Thus it is the *Eddas*, the *Volsunga Saga*, and the *Nibelungenlied* that form the main corpus of the Volsung and Nibelung stories.

Mention should be made of the *Vilkina Saga*, the saga of Dietrich of Bern, a work dealing with the Volsung story and founded upon the oral traditions and songs of the people of Bremen and Muenster, but compiled and written down in either Norway or Denmark (*ca.* 1250). Its material supplies a north German supplement to the south German *Nibelung-*

enlied to which its version of the tale provides some fascinating variants. However, this introduction will limit its examination of the German tradition to the more famous *Nibelungenlied*.

3

There are several points in the *Volsunga Saga* where its plot is far from clear. Here, however, it would be helpful to outline the story simply, without stressing the equivocal nature of certain trouble spots which will, in any case, be examined later on.

I

The Line of the Volsungs. The family whose history is traced by this saga is descended from the god Odin. Sigi, his son, becomes king of the Huns. Sigi's son and successor, Rerir, endures a childless marriage until Odin and Freyia send Ljod with a magic apple for his queen, who eats of it and becomes pregnant. For six winters she carries her child, during which time Rerir dies. She orders the child to be cut from her, and Volsung is born. He becomes a mighty king and weds Ljod. To them are born Sigmund and his twin sister Signy, who along with nine other sons form the powerful and cunning Volsung clan.

The Marriage of Signy. King Volsung builds a hall whose center is filled by the trunk of a giant oak called Branstock. He betroths the reluctant Signy to Siggeir, king of the Goths. Into the hall at their wedding feast strides a one-eyed stranger bearing a sword which he thrusts into the Branstock, declaring that it will belong to whoever can draw it forth. The stranger, Odin, vanishes. Many tug at the hilt, but only Sigmund frees the blade. Siggeir offers to buy the sword and, angered by Sigmund's proud refusal, plans revenge. Foreseeing calamity, Signy pleads with her father to undo the wedding, but Volsung stands upon his oath. Before departing for Gothland with his bride, Siggeir invites the Volsung family to visit him in three months.

The Volsungs set out. Signy meets them secretly to warn of perfidy, but her father refuses to flee. Siggeir attacks and King Volsung is slain and his ten sons taken prisoner.

The Avenging of Volsung. Sigmund and his brothers are locked in stocks in the forest, and on each of nine successive nights a she-wolf, believed to be Siggeir's mother, comes and devours one son. Now only Sigmund remains. Helped by a servant of Signy, who smears his mouth with honey, he catches the wolf's tongue in his jaws as she goes after the sweet. In the ensuing tug of war the stocks are pulled asunder, and the she-wolf's tongue is ripped from her mouth.

The liberated Sigmund hides in the forest for many years while Siggeir believes all male Volsungs dead. As each of her two sons by Siggeir reaches the age of ten, Signy sends him to Sigmund's forest-house where his valor is tested. Both are short of the Volsung standard, and at their mother's request Sigmund destroys them.

Signy realizes that only a full-blooded Volsung will avail for her plan of revenge. She changes shapes with a witch and, thus disguised, goes to Sigmund's hut where she asks shelter. After three nights with him she returns to Siggeir's house and to her true shape. Signy bears a son named Sinfjotli. When he is ten years old, he too is sent to Sigmund and successfully undergoes the trials. He remains in the forest and is hardened by Sigmund, who believes him Siggeir's son.

They have many adventures and roam for a time as werewolves. To avenge the death of Volsung, they appear at Siggeir's house, where at Signy's bidding Sinfjotli slays her children by the king and throws their bodies at his feet. Although the two heroes are captured, Signy smuggles Sigmund's sword into their prison, and they cut their way out and set fire to Siggeir's hall. Signy reveals that she and Sigmund are Sinfjotli's parents, rejoices in the avenging of her father, and then re-enters the burning hall to perish with her husband.

Helgi, Son of Sigmund. With Sinfjotli, Sigmund returns to the land of the Huns, where he becomes a mighty king and marries Borghild. They have two sons, Helgi and Hamund. Helgi slays King Hunding, and on leaving the battlefield meets the fair Sigrun, who, promised in marriage to a prince she abhors, pleads for Helgi's aid. He collects a fleet, sails against her suitor, defeats him, and marries her.

The Death of Sinfjotli. Sinfjotli kills the brother of his stepmother, Borghild, who then demands his exile. Although seemingly appeased by the payment of weregild, she poisons him at her brother's funeral feast. Sigmund carries his dead son to a wood where a man in a boat offers to ferry the body across the fjord that lies ahead. Corpse—and god, for it is Odin—vanish before Sigmund's eyes. He drives away Queen Borghild.

The Fall of Sigmund. Sigmund now woos Hjordis. His rival is King Lyngi, son of that Hunding killed by Helgi. Hjordis chooses the old but famous Sigmund. The rejected Lyngi gathers an army to attack Sigmund. Odin appears to reclaim his gift of the sword once pulled from the tree. It bursts, and Sigmund lies wounded as victorious Lyngi seeks the Volsung wealth. Hjordis, now pregnant, comes to her dying husband, who gives her the fragments of his shattered sword, Gram, and predicts that they will be fused once again to be brandished in great deeds by their son.

The Viking ships of Alf, heir of Denmark's King Hjalprek, arrive; he learns from Hjordis and her servant of Sigmund's fall. Shown where the Volsung treasure is hidden, he sails for home with it and the women.

II

The Young Sigurd. In Denmark Hjordis gives birth to Sigurd, Sigmund's son. Sigurd is educated by Regin, the king's master-smith. At Regin's urging, he requests a mount, and Odin appears to help him select the great horse, Grani. Regin urges Sigurd to go after the wealth of the dragon, Fafnir. And when Sigurd asks Regin why he incites a lad still young and inexperienced to such dangerous deeds, Regin tells his tale:

Regin's Narrative. He, Regin, was the youngest son of Hreidmar; his brothers were Fafnir, the eldest and most powerful, and Otter, a great fisherman who during the day transformed himself into an otter to fish at the river. Nearby was a waterfall in which lived and fished the dwarf, Andvari, who had assumed the likeness of a pike. Otter frequently poached in the dwarf's waterfall and then brought his booty to the river bank.

One day, as Otter was slumbering after a successful catch,

the gods, Odin, Loki, and Hoenir, came by. Loki killed Otter with a stone, and the gods skinned him. Going on with their prize, they sought hospitality at Hreidmar's house. The father, to their misfortune recognizing the otter skin, seized the gods and demanded that as weregild for his slain son his empty skin be filled and covered with gold. Loki was dispatched for the ransom. Borrowing the net of the sea goddess, Ran, he dipped into the waterfall, captured the pike-dwarf, and forced him to yield up his great treasure. Only one golden ring remained to the dwarf, and this too Loki made him surrender. Then Andvari put a curse upon both gold and ring that they should bring destruction to those who possessed them.

The gods stuffed and covered the otter skin with the gold. Hreidmar demanded that the ring be used to hide Otter's last visible whisker. Andvari's curse was soon fulfilled. Fafnir slew his father, pre-empted the hoard, and transformed himself into a dragon the better to guard it. Thus was Regin robbed of his inheritance.

The Slaying of Fafnir. Having heard the tale, Sigurd understands Regin's desire that he slay Fafnir. But first he needs a sword, which Regin promises to forge. His attempts fail, and Sigurd goes to his mother, Hjordis, to beg the fragments of Sigmund's sword. With these Regin fashions Gram anew.

Sigurd first avenges his father's death by destroying Lyngi and his clan. Then he and Regin go to Fafnir's lair, where Regin gives him treacherous advice so that he might perish in the expiring monster's blood; but Odin appears and advises him to dig a series of pits into which the blood may drain. Sigurd slays Fafnir, who before dying warns of the gold's curse. Regin congratulates Sigurd upon his victory and asks him to roast the dragon's heart. Touching it in order to see whether it is properly cooked, Sigurd then brings his finger to his mouth. A taste of the bubbling heart-blood of the dragon enables him to understand the language of the birds. They advise him to gain wisdom by eating of the heart, to kill the false Regin and become lord of the hoard, and then with the gold to seek a maid whom Odin has cast into slumber upon a flaming mountain. Following their counsel, Sigurd sets out with the hoard on Grani's back to find the sleeping valkyrie.

The Awakening of Brynhild. Upon Hindfell, a mountain in the land of the Franks, flames a great fire through which he passes. He enters a castle where he sees a sleeping warrior whose helmet and byrny he removes to discover, not a man, but the maid Brynhild. She awakens and joyfully greets him.

She relates how she had defied Odin and given victory in battle to a king whom the god had destined for defeat; angered by her disobedience, he had cast her into sleep upon the mountain and declared that she was no longer a valkyrie and would be upon awakening condemned to matrimony. However, the fire had guarded her vow never to marry one who knew the name of fear. She then teaches many things to Sigurd from her great store of runic knowledge, and they exchange vows.

Sigurd then travels to Hlymdale, where he dwells for a time with Heimir, who is to Brynhild both foster-father and brother-in-law. Brynhild soon follows and at their second meeting voices to Sigurd her fears that fate opposes their union. She predicts that he will marry another, but he will have none but Brynhild. When they have repeated their vows, he gives her Andvari's fateful golden ring taken from Fafnir's hoard.

Sigurd's Marriage. The story now turns to the family of King Giuki, who rules south of the Rhine. His three sons are Gunnar, Hogni, and Guttorm; in addition there are Gudrun, his fair daughter, and Grimhild, his cunning queen.

Gudrun, suffering from bad dreams, goes to consult Brynhild, who foresees in them both her rivalry with Gudrun and the tragic end of the Giukungs.

Sigurd leaves Hlymdale, carrying with him the cursed treasure. He arrives at Giuki's court and dwells there. Queen Grimhild, coveting Sigurd's wealth and wishing to bind him in marriage to Gudrun and in service to the realm, gives him a drink which erases all memory of Brynhild. He takes Gudrun as wife and holds dominion as a prince of the land.

The Wooing of Brynhild. Grimhild now suggests to Gunnar that he woo Brynhild with Sigurd's help. Though both King Budli, Brynhild's father, and Heimir bless the proposal, the latter cautions that the proud and independent maid has vowed to marry only that hero who can gain her fire-encircled hall. When Gunnar and Sigurd approach this fantastic residence, Gunnar's horse balks at the blaze, and Grani, whom he borrows from Sigurd, will not stir with any rider but his own master.

Now the teaching of the enchantress, Grimhild, is put to use. Sigurd assumes Gunnar's likeness and, mounted on Grani, passes through the flames. Brynhild is amazed to see him but, reminded of her oath to submit to him who dared the fire, she yields. For three nights they sleep side by side but with the sword, Gram, between them. To Sigurd, whom she takes for Gunnar, Brynhild returns Andvari's golden ring. Sigurd then leaves and reassumes his own shape.

Brynhild quits her castle to visit Heimir, to whom she confides that she had expected Sigurd, not Gunnar, to brave the flames. To his care she entrusts Aslaug, her daughter by Sigurd; for there had evidently been more than heroic colloquy between them on Hindfell. Then she, her father Budli, and her brother Atli travel to the Giukung hall for her marriage to Gunnar. When they are joined, Sigurd's memory of Brynhild returns but, helpless, he remains silent.

The Queen's Quarrel. One day while bathing in the Rhine, Brynhild wades farther upstream than Gudrun. When asked why she does so, Brynhild replies that precedence in this matter is hers since her father Budli is a greater king than Giuki and her husband Gunnar is the valiant who defied the fire, while Sigurd is merely a bondman of the Danish king. Gudrun becomes enraged and in her fury lets escape the secret that it was Sigurd in Gunnar's shape who did the deed. In proof she triumphantly holds up the golden ring which the hero of the flames had been given by Brynhild and which in turn Sigurd had given her. The crushed Brynhild returns home.

The next day more harsh words are exchanged. Brynhild threatens that Gudrun will pay for the deceit. She upbraids Gunnar for making a mockery of her oath to marry the noblest man and, perceiving the stratagem of the charmed drink, she reviles Grimhild. When her attempt to slay Gunnar is frustrated, she turns to mourning and lamentation.

To Sigurd she reveals that she never loved Gunnar. Sigurd offers her the hoard if she will leave talk of death and live with all in peace. Though admitting his love, he recognizes that they are victims of wiles from which neither can escape. He has grieved that she is not his wife but has made the best of things, consoled that at least they were together in the same house. He wishes to make love to her, but she will not deceive Gunnar and persists in her intention to die in expiation of her broken oath. To dissuade her Sigurd even offers to put aside Gudrun; but Brynhild's purpose is set.

The Deaths of Sigurd and Brynhild. Brynhild banishes Gunnar from her bed and threatens him with the public shame of her departure unless he kills Sigurd, for, she says, he was betrayed by the hero during those three nights in her castle. Since Gunnar and Hogni are bound to Sigurd by oaths, they incite their brother Guttorm to do the murder. He slays the sleeping Sigurd, whose young son, Sigmund, Brynhild also causes to be slain.

Brynhild then reproaches Gunnar for breaking his vows in bringing to pass Sigurd's death. Now that her awful work is done, she maintains that Sigurd was true to his friendship during the wooing. Predicting the sorrows of the Giukungs, she plunges a sword into herself. Her request that she be burned as Sigurd's wife on his funeral pyre is fulfilled, and she is placed next to him, a sword between them as once before.

III

Gudrun's Marriage to Atli. In sorrow Gudrun leaves her father's hall and wanders to the Danish court of King Alf where Sigurd was born. Grimhild advises her sons to follow Gudrun there with gold and silver to buy forgiveness for the death of her husband and son. A great retinue arrives in Denmark. Gunnar gives Gudrun a drink that obliterates any memory of her family's guilt. Then Grimhild forces the unwilling widow to accept Brynhild's brother Atli as her husband, and the Giukungs set out for the wedding feast at his stronghold.

Gudrun's life with Atli is unhappy. The king's sleep is troubled by dreams that forbode his death and the slaying of his children.

Atli ponders the means by which to secure the hoard of

Andvari, now the inheritance of his wife but still held by her Giukung brothers. He decides to invite them to a feast ostensibly in their honor and sends his messenger, Vingi, to bid them come. Gudrun attempts to put them on guard by sending runes of warning, but Vingi alters them to runes of welcome. Hogni is suspicious, for among the gifts sent by Atli he notices a wolf's hair, a caveat attached by Gudrun to a certain golden ring. But Gunnar in the enthusiasm of drink believes Vingi's claim that Atli, now growing old, wishes to invest the Giukungs with the custody of his lands, and accepts the invitation. Hogni's wife discovers that Gudrun's runes have been falsified, but, despite her ominous dreams and those of Gunnar's wife, the Giukungs set sail.

The Battle in Atli's Castle. As soon as they enter Atli's castle, he demands the golden hoard. The battle begins, and Gudrun dons armor to fight for her kin. The struggle is fierce, and finally of the Giukungs only Gunnar and Hogni remain. Both are captured. Atli requires that Gunnar tell where the treasure is hidden, and his reply is a request first to see his brother's heart. The heart of a thrall is brought to him, but Gunnar recognizes the deceit. And so Hogni's heart is cut from him as he laughs at his tormentors. Beholding it, Gunnar cries that now he alone knows and will never divulge where the gold lies sunken in the Rhine's depths. Atli orders him to be thrown with bound arms into a pit of serpents. Gudrun sends him a harp on which he plays with his toes so enchantingly that the vipers are lulled to sleep—all except an adder which stings him to the heart.

Gudrun's Revenge. Gudrun holds the funeral feast of her brothers. In the evening she takes her two children by Atli and cuts their throats; from their heads she fashions beakers in which she offers Atli drink; their hearts she roasts and feeds to him. When he has drunk and eaten, she reveals the horror of her work. Then at night with the help of Nibelung, the son of Hogni, she plunges a sword through her sleeping husband and sets fire to his hall, wherein his followers also perish.

Gudrun then goes down to the sea and attempts to end her life; but mighty waves carry her along and bear her to the fortress of King Jonakr. He marries her, and she bears him three sons, Hamdir, Sorli, and Erp. With them also lives Swanhild, Gudrun's daughter by Sigurd.

The Fall of the Giukungs. A king named Jormunrek, desiring the beautiful Swanhild as wife, sends his son Randver as ambassador to woo and fetch her. With him travels Bikki, the king's counselor. Their mission is successful; but Bikki suggests to the youthful Randver that it would be more fitting for him to wed the beautiful girl. Randver and Swanhild fall in love. When they arrive home, the false Bikki tells Jormunrek what has happened, and enraged he orders his son to the gallows. Upon Bikki's urging, Swanhild is bound to the fortress gates and trampled to death by horses.

When Gudrun hears of this, she arms and dispatches Hamdir and Sorli to avenge their sister, but warns that stones may be their undoing. On the way they meet their brother Erp, whose aid they ask; but, misunderstanding his cryptic reply, they slay him. Invading Jormunrek's abode, they cut off his hands and feet. Jormunrek's men cannot subdue them. But Odin, disguised as a one-eyed ancient, appears and reveals that the brothers may be destroyed only by stones. The warriors set them flying thick and fast and bring to an end the race of the Giukungs.

The *Volsunga Saga* thus falls into three parts: The heart of the story, the tragic love of Sigurd and Brynhild, occupies the central position; it is preceded by an introductory group of tales relating the heroic deeds of Sigurd's ancestors, notably those of his father, Sigmund, and of his half-brothers, Sinfjotli and Helgi, and is followed by a narration of the greed and violence that come after Sigurd's death.

The introductory section is the most primitive; its character is wild and daemonic. Sigmund, his fearful bride-sister Signy, and their offspring Sinfjotli inhabit the dark world of witches and werewolves. It is from this portion of the *Volsunga Saga* that Wagner derived material for the first act of *The Valkyrie* wherein Signy is called Sieglinde, the name of Sigmund's wife in the *Nibelungenlied*.

There are no Eddic sources for the earliest chapters of the saga in which Sigmund's ancestry is traced to the god Odin. This genealogical tree appears to be an original creation of the sagaman; such a literary technique is familiar in classical mythology and history, and its full significance here will be touched upon later.

A remark must be made about Helgi, Sigmund's son by Borghild, who suddenly fades from the tale after his winning of Sigrun. Actually Helgi was a Danish hero, the son of King Halfdan. Accounts of his deeds were traveling to Norway and the Atlantic isles at the very time that Sigurd's story was moving northward from its Rhenish home. It is not surprising that the adventures of both were confounded and the two traditions mixed, Helgi and Sigrun, Sigurd and Brynhild; moreover, the *Elder Edda* reveals that Sigrun was a valkyrie.

Sigurd, the seed of Sigmund's old age, is immensely more human than his fabulous father; his story, the middle section or nucleus of the *Volsunga Saga,* rises to heights of nobility and sacrifice from his awakening of Brynhild on the slopes of Hindfell to her grandiose death.

When the *Nibelungenlied* was created, the primeval first section still so vital in the north seems to have all but vanished from German folklore; also absent was the pivotal scene on Hindfell of the middle section of the *Volsunga Saga,* an omission which renders the relationship between the hero and Brynhild most ambiguous in the German poem.

The third section of the saga lies within the compass of recorded history. The story of Sigurd is over, and the world of myth has been left behind. Amidst forces of avarice and revenge, further adventures of his hapless widow are pursued. These gory final episodes, probably later additions to the original cycle of Eddic poems, can be linked with certain chronicled events. It is to the historical element in the *Volsunga Saga* that attention is now directed.

4

Mention has been made of the heroic age of the Germanic tribes, the fifth and sixth centuries. Confined by the Romans to the south and west and by the Huns to the east, these peoples nevertheless moved over large areas of Europe, engaging in strife among themselves and with their powerful neighbors. These struggles provided the raw materials of the sagas and epics being shaped by an incipient national consciousness. Tales of valor based upon actual happenings were embellished in the retelling and were eventually mixed with myths already ancient; finally the tales were transformed by poetic imagination. By such a process was the *Volsunga Saga* formed.

Here history and myth were mingled; the fall of the Burgundians was united with the legend of Sigurd. A tremendous calamity, not a victory, so imprinted itself upon the mind of a nation that it preserved the story, transformed it into a heroic epic by adding fantasies of its own creation, and then grafted onto the whole the legend of a sun god, Sigurd.

During the early part of the fifth century the Burgundians, an eastern Germanic tribe, moved from the Baltic and established themselves in the fertile areas on the Rhine near the modern city of Worms. In 435 they rose against the Roman governor Aëtius. Within two years the dreaded Huns, acting as agents of the Empire, practically annihilated them, the few that remained retreating towards Savoy and the banks of the Rhône.

The neighbors of this unfortunate tribe were the Franks, clustered in the Cologne area. It was they who, in a kind of fascinated horror, preserved the most intense memories of the Burgundian fall.

Attila, the famous Hunnic king, whose gothic name was a diminutive of *Atta*, meaning father, was not present at the action, but imagination soon placed the great man there. He ruled an empire that stretched from the Caspian to the Rhine. In 451, allied with tributary Germans, he crossed into Gaul, which he laid waste. At Châlons, one of history's decisive battles, his progress was checked by Aëtius and his Visigothic allies.

In the west Attila's name gathered a terrible fame; in the east he was revered as a benevolent ruler. It is not surprising that he achieved a secure but antithetical place in Teutonic legend—as the cruel Atli of the *Volsunga Saga* on the one hand and as the noble Etzel of the *Nibelungenlied* on the other. The former work had its origins among those west German tribes who feared his enmity; the *Nibelungenlied* was given its final form in Austria (not far from the site of

Attila's old capital near present-day Budapest) where the tradition of his magnanimity still persisted.

The historical Attila may certainly be linked with events in the *Volsunga Saga*. Atli's murder of Gunnar and Hogni is a survival of the catastrophe of Worms.

In 453 the king of the Huns married a German princess named Hildico. After the wedding feast he retired to bed, hemorrhaged, and died in a pool of blood. Poetic imagination was soon at work on the facts; rumours gathered that Hildico had killed the great Hun to avenge the deaths of her Germanic kinsmen who fell at Worms; to the violent tale, already being embroidered with Attila's presence, was added a dénouement of revenge. The whole was made more compact by turning Hildico into a princess of the Burgundians, sister to the fallen kings. Thus there gradually took shape the heroic figures of fierce Atli, his victims, Gunnar and Hogni, and their vengeful sister Gudrun, bride of the king. That the conflict was originally with Rome was forgotten. Characters were mixed and chronology confused.

It is interesting to note that in the *Nibelungenlied* Gudrun is called Kriemhild and that Hildico is a diminutive of this name's suffix which means "battle."

There are further similarities to recorded history in the *Volsunga Saga*. Jordanes, the gothic historian who left the famous description of Attila at the battle of Châlons, also relates a story of Ermanaric, king of the enormous Ostrogothic realm of the fourth century: he ordered a woman, Sunhilda, to be rent by horses as a punishment for her husband's perfidy; her brothers Sarus and Ammius sought retaliation. Jormunrek is Norse for Ermanaric; the parallel to Swanhild and her brothers Sorli and Hamdir is also clear.

The unfortunate Ermanaric, who actually took his life (*ca*. 374) rather than witness the destruction of his kingdom by the Huns, became a symbol of selfishness and villainy in the Teutonic tradition. Not only were events concerning him grafted on to the saga of Sigurd, but in other tales he was converted into the wicked uncle of the noble Theodoric the Ostrogoth (Dietrich of Bern).

And just as stories of Jormunrek and Atli were attached to

those of Sigurd's daughter Swanhild and her mother Gudrun, so Aslaug, his daughter by Brynhild, became the link between the mythical world of her parents and the semi-historical adventures of her husband, Ragnar Lodbrok. More will be said of Aslaug later in connection with William Morris' poem about her.

King Giuki and his sons Gunnar and Guttorm may certainly be brought into relationship with the historical Burgundian princes Gibica, Gundahari, and Godomar who are mentioned in the *Lex Burgundionum*. Gundahari was the ruler destroyed by the Huns in 437. He is, of course, Gunther of the *Nibelungenlied* and survives as a high baritone in Wagner's *The Nibelung's Ring*. A third prince, Gislahari, is immortalized as the youthful and fair Giselher of the *Nibelungenlied*, wherein Hogni of the *Volsunga Saga* appears as the fierce and clever Hagen.

The central characters of the saga, Sigurd and Brynhild, represent an interesting combination of the historical, mythical, and literary, though the latter two elements dominate. They have no demonstrable forbears in history although it is tempting to recall Sigebert, King of Austrasia, the easternmost part of the Frankish lands, which had Metz as its capital; he took to wife a Visigothic princess named Brunhilda; his arms were victorious against the Avars, Danes, and Saxons, and it was told that he uncovered a hidden treasure. In 575 he fell to assassins dispatched by his sister-in-law, Fredegond.

Despite this alluring parallel, Sigurd is essentially a creature springing from myth, a symbol of nature, rebirth, and light. To rise, the day must kill the dragon of mist and then awaken the sun-maiden who slumbers on the heights. It is a fleeting victory and joy, for the awakener must soon succumb to those dark and obscure forces that make the sun sink beneath the horizon. Every day he is reborn to accomplish his task. The symbol was anthropomorphized: Sigurd, the hero of light, was called into being; the nature myth became the heroic saga. It was probably among the Franks of the Rhine that this change first took place.

Through the missionary activities of the Roman legionnaires, elements of the eastern sun god, Mithras, whose cult of endurance and courage was widespread among the Im-

perial soldiery, may have entered into the creation of Sigurd.
It is in Germany that the greatest number of Mithraeums
have been uncovered; the popularity of its rites among the
Teutons is indisputable. It is interesting to speculate that
Sigurd may be in part an extension or remote product of
the Persian Zend-Avesta of Babylonian origin, and that not
only Balder of the Aesir but also Shamas of the Assyrians
may be reflected in the hero.

It is certainly possible that elements of King Sigebert's
career eventually became part of the story. The rival queens,
Fredegond, Sigebert's murderer, and his widow, Brunhilda,
fanned many internal conflicts. In 613 Brunhilda, at three
score and ten, finally met a ghastly end on a flaming pyre
when the Frankish nobles, incensed over her murder of ten
members of the royal dynasty, condemned her to three days
of torture and the humiliation of being led through camp on
a camel; she was then torn by wild horses and her remains
given to the fire.

Brynhild of the saga is also both advocate and victim of
a grim philosophy. Fierce, unyielding, proud, and courageous,
capable of great love and devastating wrath—to avenge her
hurt and her broken oath, she works the destruction of the
man who unwittingly betrayed her and married another; she
then kills herself and, in accordance with her wish, is burned
on his pyre as his wife.

There is a scene, outwardly somewhat similar, in an earlier
part of the *Volsunga Saga* where Signy, exultantly viewing
the burning of her hated husband's hall, tastes her triumph
for an expansive moment and then turns to join him in the
flames. The code of consanguinity formed her hate, and another set of moral obligations guided her to the fire. Brynhild,
too, followed a philosophy of retribution, but a wild and
consuming love drew her to the blazing bier. Her solution to
the emotional and moral dilemma in which she found herself
was that of Wagner's Isolde, death for both. Sigurd saw the
issue clearly: "Thou wilt not live when I am dead; the days
of our two lives shall be few enough from henceforth."
Brynhild's hate, springing from her love, and her transfigured
death make her one of the great women of literature. Although it is hard to ignore the historical analogies, one feels

that she was born neither of myth nor history but rather of a poet's observation of the human condition. As Sigurd has often been called the Achilles of the North, certainly Brynhild brings to mind elements of Lady Macbeth and Medea.

There remains the etremely knotty problem of identifying the Giukungs and Nibelungs. In the *Volsunga Saga* Gunnar and Hogni, the sons of King Giuki, are called, after him, Giukungs. Hogni's son was Nibelung (he who helped Gudrun slay Atli). Evidently in time his name also became attached to the Rhenish tribe. Snorri Sturluson in the *Younger Edda* tells us that "Gunnar and Hogni were called Nibelungs or Giukungs; therefore the gold is called the Nibelungen hoard or inheritance." It would seem, therefore, that in general the terms Giukung and Nibelung were interchangeable.

The word "Nibelung" is a patronymic derived from *nebel* meaning mist or fog. The Nibelungs are thus associated with darkness and obscurity, and it is appropriate that Sigurd the hero of light, the second Balder, should succumb to their plots. Indeed, ancient Teutonic myth relates that before the creation of earth and sky a place of shadows and clouds called Niflheim was situated north of the great void. Niflheim became associated with the land of the dead. It was a dank place inhabited by giants and dwarfs, in which was situated the kingdom of the goddess Hel, whose gates were guarded by the fearful dog, Garm.

In the *Nibelungenlied,* the name Nibelung presents further problems. Early in the poem Nibelung appears, not as a Rhenish Burgundian, but as one of two brother princes who rule the Nibelungs, a people made up of ordinary mortals, giants, and dwarfs. Siegfried (Sigurd) slays the brothers and wins both the hoard and the allegiance of this motley nation. After this he travels to the Burgundian court on the Rhine.

To the reader's confusion, in the second part of the poem there is no longer a clear distinction between the Nibelungen land and people conquered by Siegfried and the Rhenish nation and family into which he married. The names of the two are confused, and the Burgundians are frequently identified as Nibelungs perhaps, as Richard Wagner would suggest in his essay *The Nibelungs,* because the hoard is now in the family's possession. Yet Wagner ignores the fact that the most famous owner of the treasure, Siegfried himself, is never referred to as a Nibelung; true, he is called *helt von Niblungelant* or hero of Nibelung land, but this is a title referring to his exploits in reducing this nation to vassalage.

The final strophe of the poem as it survives in various manuscripts describes its action as either *der Nibelunge liet,* i.e. *The Song of the Nibelungs,* or as *der Nibelunge nôt,* i.e. *The Fall of the Nibelungs,* both of which variant readings designate the Burgundian dynasty as Nibelung.

The thirteenth century compilers of the poem were themselves very unclear about the name; how much more difficult today to find one's way through this mixture of allusions compounded over the ages.

It has been remarked that Gibica was one of the historical rulers of the Burgundians. Around his name and deeds gathered some of the legends and symbols of centuries. It was evidently from Gibica that Wagner derived "Gibichungs," his term in *The Nibelung's Ring* for the Giukungs of the *Volsunga Saga.* Obviously he could not use the term "Nibelung" for his Rhenish royal family, for in the very first scene of his cycle he had returned the Nibelungs to their ultimate origins as dwarfs toiling in the dim, rocky, and vaporous caverns of the underworld.

5

Earlier the observation was made that the *Volsunga Saga* suffers from various ambiguities. Most of the difficulty gathers around Brynhild and the ill-defined relationships among members of her family. She has as father the royal Budli, a vague figure who for some reason did not raise his daughter; she boasts a foster-father, Heimir, who doubles as a brother-in-law; his wife, Bekkhild stays at home while sister Brynhild fares to the wars as a valkyrie—a profession which further implies a filial association of some sort with Odin. An unsuccessful assimilation of northern and southern, i.e. German, traditions is the cause of Brynhild's rich, varied, and equivocal parentage; this in turn is the root of the sagaman's troubles in achieving a completely unified narrative and must be the focal point of any consideration of problems of reference and continuity in the saga.

Many questions that the saga inspires, it responds to with equivocations. Its sources must supply whatever answers there are. Like the drama of Wagner the *Volsunga Saga* can only be fully understood through an examination of the works which formed it.

Brynhild's Eddic background will now be explored as well as the influence it had in the *Volsunga Saga* and, most curiously, the *Nibelungenlied*.

As the saga unfolds, an attentive reader may occasionally feel it necessary to retrace his steps in order to clarify a phrase or dialogue which at first glance seems unrelated to what has gone before. This confusion arises in the *Volsunga Saga* whenever varying and frequently irreconcilable versions of the same incidents are combined.

Six hundred years later Wagner, despite his free and rhapsodic approach to the myth, could not completely resolve similar problems provoked by an inherited store of inconsistent traditions. Wagner seems to court confusion as he spreads differing explanations of the same occurrence throughout the vast dimension of the *Ring*. Moreover, in his final text he retains fleeting references to passages rejected from earlier drafts.

Parallel situations exist in the *Volsunga Saga*. Despite the skill of the author all the disparate threads do not knit together. Events are accounted for here by one cause and there by another; some of the fundamental points of the tale are beset by ambiguity. For example, most significant and discomforting are the reader's doubts as to the relationship between Brynhild and Sigurd. The basic and vexing question is—who *is* Brynhild?

Whatever answer there is will be found in the cycle of Volsung poems in the *Elder Edda*.

In the Eddic *Lay of Fafnir*, an eagle tells Sigurd of Sigrdrifa, the slumbering Valkyrie. The story continues in the *Lay of Sigrdrifa;* Sigurd climbs the burning mountain of Hindfell to awaken her. Sigrdrifa arises and in the noble verses that Wagner paraphrased in his *Siegfried* she hails the day, the sons of day, the gods, and the bounteous earth. Her story is identical with that of Brynhild in the saga—her disobedience to Odin and her sleep guarded by fire so that none but the fearless hero might approach. According to folk tradition, one would expect the awakener to marry the awakened maid. Indeed, after the valkyrie lectures Sigurd extensively from her runic knowledge, they do exchange vows. However, armed with her enlightenment and love, he quits Hindfell and, strange to tell, Sigrdrifa passes from his life.

The woman named Brynhild, encountered in later Eddic poems, is an entirely different person. *The Short Lay of Sigurd* pictures her suffering from overmastering love for the hero. Filled with evil thoughts, she wanders in the evening over the ice-fields after he and his wife Gudrun have withdrawn to bed.

Yet the Eddic poems at times reveal certain resemblances between the vengeful Brynhild and the exhuberant Sigrdrifa. Brynhild's drive towards savage revenge is that of a spurned woman. In the above lay she declares, "O for my Sigurd! I shall have death, or my fair, my lovely, laid in mine arms. For the word once spoken, I sorrow sorely—" Could this lament refer to the vows sworn on Hindfell? Confirmation is found in the magnificent poem called *The Hell-Ride of Brynhild*; here the dead Brynhild speaks of her disobedience to Odin, her fire-guarded sleep, and her awakening by Sigurd. Certainly these are the very events experienced by Sigrdrifa. Obviously a tradition existed in which Sigrdrifa and Brynhild (or better, the awakened valkyrie and the betrayed woman) were the same character.

In contrast to this warlike valkyrie, in the Eddic poem *Gripir's Prophecy* Brynhild is described as highborn and beautiful, the daughter of a king raised in the house of royal Heimir as his ward.

It has been suggested that an error was made during the compilation of the *Elder Edda* and that "sigrdrifa" is not a proper name at all but an epithet meaning "bringer of victory" that was meant to be applied to Brynhild. This is a most welcome theory, for it reduces the confusion from three different ladies to two, both named Brynhild.

Thus the Eddic Brynhild's background is sometimes alluded to as that of a helmeted Norse valkyrie and at other times as that of a proper Rhenish Princess, a confusion resulting from an unsuccessful mixture of Scandinavian and German traditions. The Edda's greatness, however, lies in the power of its poetry and not in the consistency of its narrative.

The author of the *Volsunga Saga* elected to combine the valkyrie and princess of the Edda into one person, Brynhild, thereby giving greater unity to the tale. Some authorities believe that in doing this he returned to an earlier tradition. Whatever the case, we shall see that, leaning on the *Edda*, he retained traces of Brynhild's dual pedigree, a confusing fact which makes many motivations, episodes, and speeches equivocal and which, moreover, gives her an unduly complicated and even at times schizophrenic personality. His not too adroit manipulation of the two traditions led to some strange situations in the *Volsunga Saga*.

After the exchange of vows on Hindfell, Sigurd leaves for Hlymdale, and Brynhild follows shortly thereafter. She whom we last saw delivering heroic runic lectures is soon discovered in a tower at her needlework. Sigurd catches sight of her by chance; when he finally approaches to pay court, both act almost like strangers. In this second meeting the synthesis of valkyrie and princess fails; the author's craft is not equal to covering the joints.

Furthermore, we are never given a clear picture of Brynhild's hilltop hall. It seems as schizophrenic as she. No flames are visible during Gudrun's neighborly visit, but they roar with fury when Gunther comes wooing. The disguised Sigurd breaks through them a second time and finds Brynhild, not at her embroidery as at Hlymdale, but with sword in hand, once more the helmeted warrior-maid of Hindfell.

Yet another old Eddic tradition, alien to the coherence of the saga, is suggested by the author. In one of her great tirades (Chapter 29), Brynhild states that she was forced by her father, King Budli, to marry Gunnar, for the latter and King Giuki threatened war if she did not yield; it was at this time, she continues, that she vowed to wed whosoever would ride Grani through the fire. This directly contradicts Budli's gentle acquiescence to his daughter's wishes as described in an earlier section of the saga (Chapter 27):

"But he said withal that so high-minded was she, that that man only might wed her whom she would."

The *Short Lay of Sigurd* in the *Elder Edda* relates that Atli, when set upon by the Giukungs, who demanded his sister, tricked her into believing that the radiant hero bearing the trophies of Fafnir was really Gunnar. To the man with this name she unsuspectingly allowed herself to be promised; thus was the siege lifted and Brynhild betrayed.

It is to this version of the wooing of Brynhild, one that omits the magic exchanges of semblances, that the sagaman suddenly and inconsistently turned when writing Brynhild's speech.

In her outburst Brynhild compounds the reader's confusion by declaring that the ring came to her through her father. Later (Chapter 32) she alludes to similar extraneous events, old strains of almost forgotten versions of the tale which rise to the surface and claim their rights.

The author of the *Volsunga Saga* may be criticized for not guarding the coherence of his tale more closely; but so great is the vivacity and rapidity of his narrative that despite the flaws one is carried along by its animated current.

The *Nibelungenlied* retains similar residual remains of earlier traditions. The beauty of its verses aside, the German poem lacks the over-all unity of the *Volsunga Saga*, for the encounter on Hindfell is elided as is the primeval curse on the gold. The *Nibelungenlied* is dominated by the attempt of Gudrun, now called Kriemhild, to achieve vengeance for the murder of her husband. Brynhild disappears from significant action midway in the tale. Yet a strange, undefined, but strongly felt link between Brynhild and Siegfried (Sigurd) causes the quarrel between the queens whose bloody consequence was the death of many men and the fall of the kingdom of the Rhine. Brynhild, who ages before was the valkyrie on Hindfell, once again lays claim to her first love, and the author or authors of the *Nibelungenlied* are helpless to control the situation.

It is possible that a kind of censorship was brought to bear upon whatever remained of the older Norse tradition of the tale in an effort to expunge elements that might offend ladies of the chivalric age. Yet, although the poem represents a weakening of the heroic tradition, it nevertheless confirms by fascinating indirection the early acquaintance of Brynhild and Sigurd as revealed in the *Volsunga Saga.*

Although there is no direct reference in the *Nibelungenlied* to any relationship between Brynhild and Siegfried before his journey to Iceland to woo her for Gunther (Gunnar), there are oblique allusions which affirm the old tie.

When Gunther's plan to court Brynhild is first discussed, his vassal Hagen remarks that it would be wise to ask Siegfried to share the adventure since he knows much about the Icelandic queen; yet, how and where he gained this knowledge is not revealed. Furthermore, Siegfried's familiarity with the buildings and customs of Brynhild's capital at Isenstein and his ability to identify her among a throng of maidens suggests some previous acquaintance. Moreover, the Brynhild of the *Nibelungenlied* retains the amazon traits of a valkyrie. She is skilled at hurling the stone and throwing the spear, and to win her a suitor must surpass her at these sports or forfeit his life. Siegfried wins her fraudulently for Gunther through the trickery of the magic cloud-cloak or *Tarnkappe;* we are reminded of the Greek story of Melanion, who with the aid of Aphrodite's golden apples defeats and wins the cruel Atalanta at a foot race.

The *Nibelungenlied's* most astounding and somewhat ludicrous remnant of Brynhild's Eddic valkyrie background is her wrestling match with Gunther on their bridal couch; she binds him with her silk girdle and hangs him helpless from a wall hook. It is significant that her rage was kindled by the announcement of Siegfried's betrothal to Kriemhild (Gudrun). She rationalizes her resentment on the level of court etiquette, but one senses a deeper cause. It was Siegfried, not Gunther, whom she had expected to solicit her hand when the ship from the Rhine anchored at her citadel. She evidently remembered Hindfell of the *Edda* and *Volsunga Saga;* the old tradition would not die.

6

Comparing certain literary and ethical aspects of the *Volsunga Saga* and the *Nibelungenlied* will serve to throw into relief particular qualities of both.

It would be unprofitable to judge at the outset between the vigorous prose of one and the elegant verse of the other to determine which form best suits the Rhenish tale. However, individual idioms apart, it must be observed that the two works pace their material quite differently. The *Volsunga Saga* hardly pauses for breath as its rapid action hurtles towards final calamity. Even the almost entirely descriptive section, *Of the Semblance and Array of Sigurd Fafnir's-bane* (Chapter 22), propels the story forward with a recital of the hero's growing fame.

The *Nibelungenlied*, on the contrary, all too frequently halts to dwell with tedious repetition upon details of costumes, arms, and feasts. It is, rather, a poetic romance of adventure, beautifully and simply set forth in well over two thousand rhymed quatrains. Though its origins probably lie in popular ballads passed on through the ages by oral tradition, this humble background is hardly obvious as we contemplate its aristocratic and polished form, probably created for recitation in the castle hall.

How different is the *Volsunga Saga*, which despite the appearance of the supernatural and the exaggerations of the heroic tale still reflects something of the rough life of the Norwegian refugees who settled barren Iceland, where the *Volsunga Saga* achieved written form. Those who dwelt in this craggy volcanic landscape were concerned with essentials —the success or failure of their meager crops, hunting, fishing, and the inevitable strife with their neighbors. Such was the material of the family sagas. To survive was to have hardihood. Yet the sagas stress not only strength but also individuality. Was not the colony formed by those who opposed the tyranny of King Harald? They took their ships on daring journeys to Scotland, England, and the mainland, sometimes for business, but often for plunder. On the island of ice and fire lived a defiant people, always alert against the treachery of nature and man.

But the sagas not only glorify the fearlessness and cunning of their heroes as mighty individuals; they also, as in the mythic-heroic *Volsunga Saga*, touch upon great truths— friendship and love that cannot alter, love that touches madness, perfidy from those least suspected of harboring it, the demands of duty whose price is blood. There is, moreover, a grandeur and self-exaltation in meeting death. Here is a sweeping view of life found only in the greatest literature. To compare the sagaman who compiled our tale with a poet such as Racine may at first seem far-fetched; but both poets tersely present the values of a certain society with a succinctness and condensation that are admirable. Nor are such poets lacking in feeling, for the power of the situations presented and their accompanying emotions are made doubly effective by the compressed phrases that set them forth.

It is not to be implied that the *Nibelungenlied* lacks many of the qualities credited to the *Volsunga Saga*. However, the directness of the original tale is obviously diluted in the poem both by baptizing the characters and thus translating their pagan woes into a superficially Christian environment, also by clothing the fierce tale in elegant diction and form.

In contrast, so clearly does the sagaman attempt to reproduce the spirit of the Eddic poems that scholars can occasionally detect their alliterations mirrored in the prose of the *Volsunga Saga*.

Like the sagaman, or perhaps from him, Wagner learned this power of the word that is not spoken but only felt and the beauty and persuasiveness of silence. The comparison should not be carried too far, for Wagner was able to call upon music to speak that other language which lies beneath the word. However, in *The Nibelung's Ring*, despite the popular belief in his tendencies toward expansiveness, if not downright garrulousness, he does create an almost telescopic diction in which words seem to fold one into the other.

Not only the style and spirit, but also the moral-ethical values of the *Ring* derive more from the *Volsunga Saga* of the northern peoples than from the South German *Nibelungenlied*. Before examining this ethical aspect, it would be opportune to consider how these works were judged by the morally conscious nineteenth century.

Between 1859 and 1885 (by the first date Wagner's *The Nibelung's Ring* was more than half complete) appeared Tennyson's *The Idylls of the King*, wherein the poet, for the good of his righteous readers, camouflaged the illegitimate birth of King Arthur by a plethora of conflicting tales and marvelous detail. It is not surprising that the same Victorians, so benevolently protected by Lord Tennyson, were repelled by the incestuous mating of Sigmund and his sister and found the *Volsunga Saga* and its offspring, *The Valkyrie*, equally unpalatable.

But nineteenth-century Germany did admire the Christianized society of the *Nibelungenlied* even though Goethe had warned against its barbarity. For here Germans found scenes that exalted a characteristic that they were fond of discovering and esteeming in themselves, the ancient *triuwe*, a loyalty so deep that it could be blind even to ghastly consequences. The *Nibelungenlied* furnished many horrifying, albeit Christian, examples of this particular virtue, and many a German sham-gothic arch had its spandrels painted with Nibelungen tableaux. It is interesting, on the other hand, that Morris began a translation of the *Nibelungenlied* and had finished over two hundred stanzas when he abandoned the work as uncongenial.

Morris, like Wagner, responded more to the *Volsunga Saga*, whose clearly discernible ethical design, achieved through the symbol of the golden ring, gives the work greater unity. The ring, cursed to punish its theft by the gods, eventually finds its way to Odin's offspring; prized as a love token, it yields only death. The transgression of all-father is suffered for by his progeny. Adding the godly lineage of the Volsungs to his narrative and stressing their descent from Odin, the sagaman greatly strengthened the ethical content of his work; the crime committed by the Aesir of Asgard is expiated by their descendants on earth; the stage of the drama extends from Walhall to the Rhine. The doom of the Volsungs was already closed in the primeval waterfall when the frantic dwarf, Andvari, unsuccessfully besought Loki to return the magic ring. As in the classical tale of Oedipus wherein the descendants of the House of Laius perish for abominable crimes of which they are guiltless, so Sigurd, Brynhild, and the related Giukungs, fall victims to the cursed gold.

If that "certain gold ring" to which Gudrun knit a wolf's hair for a warning of Atli's duplicity is accepted as identical with the ring cursed by Andvari—last directly mentioned in the saga when it blazed on Gudrun's hand during the queens' quarrel in the Rhine—then this theme is seen to arch over the entire tale from Andvari to the murder of the Giukung princes. It is tempting to presume that Gudrun sends the same fatal ring to her brothers and that its re-entrance into their household signals their downfall. Although there is no definite statement in the text of the *Volsunga Saga* to this effect, a passage in the *Elder Edda* does support the supposition.

The *Nibelungenlied* offers no such cosmic action. It has already been observed that the daemonic and mythical first section of the *Volsunga Saga* is missing from the *Nibelungenlied;* so also is any reference to the origins of the Nibelungen hoard and the curse upon it. The dragon remains as a strange and forelorn remnant, and even the link between him and the treasure has vanished. Although the power of the un-mentioned curse is still felt in some mysterious and atavic way, the *Nibelungenlied* is essentially a poetic romance of revenge and not a story that involves concepts of immemorial sin. Kriemhild's primary overriding need is satisfaction for her husband's murder; her desire to repossess the red Nibe-lungen gold is a minor motive. The ruin of the Burgundian knights proceeds directly from their complicity in Siegfried's death.

In the *Volsunga Saga*, on the other hand, it is Atli's greed for the treasure that destroys the dynasty of the Rhine; its fall is encompassed by the curse. Moreover, in an artful bal-ance of elements, the Thyestean feast which Gudrun pre-pares with Atli's butchered children, a deed so horrible that its telling is difficult to bear, is repaid by Odin himself, who appears to direct the destruction of her last two sons. One event anticipates and the other requites.

It was this overarching moral symbolism of the *Volsunga Saga* that attracted Wagner and entered into *The Nibelung's Ring.* His Brynhild, after Siegfried's death, reproaches the god and demands that he look down from Walhall upon his own eternal guilt; she laments that the hero had been en-meshed in the workings of the curse to which the god him-self must succumb. Indeed, Wagner found in the *Volsunga Saga* a well-built structure which he put to use and which is still clearly visible beneath the remarkable transformations he wrought upon it to fashion *The Nibelung's Ring*.

Whereas the primary theme of the *Nibelungenlied* is merely that of a woman who expends her life in unswerving devotion to her first husband's memory, ultimately bringing as an offering to this altar of love the blood of his enemies, in the more primitive *Volsunga Saga*, husband, wife, and even children are sacrificed to an overriding loyalty to kin— to parents and siblings; wedlock is the minor tie; and over this harsh world broods the dwarf's curse. The mood of anxiousness, change, and inevitability that characterizes the Eddic poems permeates the *Volsunga Saga*.

7

Wagner's *The Nibelung's Ring* also shares the atmosphere and spirit of the Eddic poems. Theirs is a world worried by the certainty of ultimate ruin; no escape is offered; the seers prophesy, and the omens multiply; all things portend the coming of an awful day when gods and men must submit to their annihilation as decreed by fate. Heroic and tragic deeds are wrought in a threatened, restless, unstable world. Literature has few more telling examples of uncertainty and disquiet than Wagner's Wotan, who attempts to govern his fear-ridden cosmos with the terrible knowledge that the gods themselves are doomed one day to go down.

The Eddic concept of *ragna rök*, the doom or twilight of the gods, greatly interested Wagner, and he gleaned much material for the *Ring* from the *Völuspa*, perhaps the greatest poem in the *Elder Edda*. Here Odin, fearful of impending disaster and desiring to know his destiny, summons from her grave a great prophetess, who rises to sing of the past and future. This poem, the bible of Norse mythology and cosmology, ends with a magnificent description of the gods' final hours.

The poet-musician was fascinated by the concept of a universal order which wore the trappings of timelessness and perpetuity but which was, beneath its outer glory, as mortal as its humblest servant. A terrible uprising would cast the eternals of Asgard from their high places. How stimulating these concepts must have been to a young man of 1848 inclined towards social revolution as well as poetry. A summary of the background and story of the *ragna rök* will show to what extent Wagner drew inspiration from the *Völuspa* and other Eddic poems. Moreover, it will enable the reader to appreciate the extraordinary way in which he utilized this material in conjunction with the *Volsunga Saga*.

The ancient Teutons believed that the universe was penetrated and supported by a gigantic ash tree named Yggdrasil, whose ever verdant foliage reached the height of the sky. Of its three mighty roots, one was nourished in the nether world; from a source near the second, which reached down to the realm of the frost giants, issued the fountain of the wise giant, Mimir, in whose waters flowed all knowledge and from which Odin, seeking knowledge of his fate, once drank at the cost of an eye; in the third root nestled the fountain of Urd, the wisest of the norns—here these goddesses of fate gathered to draw water and moisten the tree lest it wither away. On Yggdrasil's highest branch sat a golden cock, who scanned the approaches to the celestial city to warn of the inevitable arrival of the giants, the ancient enemies of the gods.

Thus the eternals lived in vigilance. In primal times the youthful Odin and his brothers, themselves descended from the race of giants, killed the giant, Ymir, progenitor of all living beings. Through this murder Odin achieved power and subjected the universe to his will. But all knew that one day the giants would gather to avenge the ancient wrong.

But even before that last terrible day the fair Aesir, who dwelt in Asgard, struggled against change and mortality. Idun, the goddess of youth, provided them with golden apples that prevented their aging. When with the complicity of the treacherous Loki she was carried off by the giant, Thjazi, the Aesir, deprived of the magic fruit, soon grew old. They saved themselves by forcing Loki to retrieve the goddess.

In one of the most amazing poems in the *Elder Edda*, Odin, in order to accomplish his own rejuvenation, wounded himself with his great spear and suspended himself from a branch of the world ash tree; for nine nights he hung there offering himself, afflicted with mortality, to himself, the eternal god. Finally, after suffering hunger and thirst, he freed himself with the aid of some magic runes and dropped to the ground, where he stood youthful, vigorous, and renewed. Thus the great god brought to pass his own resurrection.

The ash tree itself suffered change through constant assault and gave unmistakable signs that its days were not without number. Nidhögg, a serpent, gnawed at its third root, and stags devoured its new shoots and buds. The norns protected and watered the tree, and thanks to their care it throve and reared its mighty trunk in the center of the universe; it stood fast until the day the giant wolf, Fenrir, burst his fetters and shook all creation; the tree trembled and groaned from its deepest root to its highest branch. Beneath Yggdrasil lay hidden the trumpet of Heimdall, sentinel of the gods. With the crowing of the cock that announced the giants' approach this trumpet, sounding throughout the universe, was to call the eternals to arms.

But it was not only mortality and Odin's guilt in the murder of Ymir that was to cause the gods to pass away. To the Aesir could be laid other transgressions. Gullveig, the ambassadress of a rival race of gods, was tortured in order to seize her riches; by this act the Aesir brought war into the world. The hard-working giant who built Walhall was tricked out of his promised wage; by this unworthy example they weakened the moral force of treaties and agreements.

The loss of Odin's eye was but one link in the chain of calamities encompassing the gods. Perturbing dreams came to the eternals, and it was the troubled sleep of Balder, the incomparably beautiful son of Odin, that betokened the end.

Mention was made earlier of a remarkable poem called, in its translation by Thomas Gray, *The Descent of Odin*. Its original title is *Vegtamskvidha*, and it forms the fifth section of the *Elder Edda*. Here Odin in disguise descends to the underworld and by his magic compels a great wala or prophetess to awaken and unravel the mystery of the fearful dreams. He learns of Balder's inevitable death and the coming twilight of the gods. This great poem was used by Wagner as a model for the encounter between Wotan and Erda in the third act of *Siegfried*.

After Balder's death fearful omens continued to disturb the peace of Asgard. Fenrir's offspring seized the sun and plunged the world into darkness and strife. Finally Fenrir burst the marvelous chain fashioned by the dwarfs by which the gods had kept him bound. The dreaded Midgard serpent, whose coils encircled the earth, rose from the depths of the sea and advanced relentlessly upon the celestial city. Armies of giants and monsters drew near, and Heimdall's trumpet sounded. The rainbow bridge to Asgard was stormed. In the terrible battle all of the great gods perished. The fire giant, Surt, enkindled the earth; the sun was dark; the earth sank into the ocean; the bright stars fell; the all-nourishing ash tree was consumed by towering fire that played against the heavens; all living things died. Rivers and seas rose up, and boiling waves covered the traces of gods and men.

But this was not the end. There is a catharsis. The wala, whose predictions form the *Völuspa*, foresees a cosmic regeneration. Little by little, the waters recede, and earth shows itself anew. A second time, beautifully green, it rises from the ocean. And on the site of Asgard a new race of gods is seen. Radiant Balder, resurrected from Hel's kingdom, sits in Odin's high seat. All evil is amended; a mighty one will come and rule over all; he will establish a holy peace that will last forever.

8

It was only in the final stages of Wagner's work on the *Ring,* however, that he put to use this motif of redemption following ruin. Quite the opposite, his earliest poetic drama on the Nibelungen subject, *Siegfried's Death* (1848), ends triumphantly, for the gods do not fall. Brynhild joins Siegfried on his funeral pyre; the fire dissolves to vapor, and in the clouds she, in full valkyrie regalia upon her charger, draws Siegfried by the hand up to Walhall, where all will share eternal bliss. The water-maidens, riding the crest of the overflowing Rhine, bear away ring and tarnhelm. The gold is restored to its original innocence; the hero's death and Brynhild's sacrifice have released the gods from its curse.

Thus the prediction of the third norn in the opening scene has been realized—that a joyful hero whose will is free would defiantly fight for the gods and by his victory complete the deed he began. Through his deed, the slaying of Fafnir, Siegfried won the curse; his victory is his and Brynhild's deaths, which ends the need of the gods. Siegfried and Brynhild are one. Before their parting on the valkyrie rock, the ancient Hindfell, they ecstatically realize this. She is his soul, and, wherever he journeys, there travels her spirit; though physically separated, there is no parting; all his deeds shall be accomplished through her virtue. With minor changes, this scene furnished the text of the great love duet in the prologue to *The Twilight of the Gods*. Indeed, most of *Siegfried's Death* was later refashioned into this concluding drama of the *Ring*.

At this point it is advisable to examine some of the personal problems, political hopes, professional plans, and aesthetic and moral theories with which Wagner was concerned during the incubative stages and creation of *Siegfried's Death*, and above all to observe the visionary and fanatic state of mind which led him to dramatize himself as the heroic renewer. Moreover, a glance at the two prose works out of which *Siegfried's Death* grew, *The Wibelungs* and *The Nibelungen Myth as Scheme for a Drama*, will underline his singular relationship to and personal interpretation of the *Eddas* and the *Volsunga Saga*. Then, at the point where *Siegfried's Death* becomes incorporated into the new and expanding concept of *The Nibelung's Ring*, it will be advantageous to consider both Wagner's attempts to create a fitting peroration for his drama that would reconcile the sanguine and the despondent, and his amazing solution of this dilemma in which he joined *Volsunga Saga* and *Völuspa* in unprecedented union.

The Wagner of *Siegfried's Death* saw himself in the role of the hero who redeems a materialistic and base world through art. In the Eddic tales of corrupted gods he had found a parallel to the philistine and degraded officialdom of Europe, especially of his native Saxony, ready for regeneration. The Wagner of 1848 did not wish authority to wither away; reform was sufficient, though perhaps it had to be imposed by strong methods. Despite his dalliance with socialism and his friendship with such revolutionaries as Michael Bakunin, Wagner always remained essentially a monarchist and an authoritarian.

For many months before the writing of *Siegfried's Death* he had realized that his career as Kapellmeister in Dresden would never bring artistic satisfaction, and that his life's goal, the revitalizing of German culture through reform of the theatre, could come about only through political upheaval. His practical program for the improvement of the opera orchestra had been rejected, and in 1848 his plan for the organization of a national theatre was ignored. Disillusioned, he believed that the courtiers who directed the theatre had betrayed their trust; in their unqualified hands was what he believed to be the divine instrument of German rebirth, the opera house; if recast along Wagnerian lines, it could fulfill its lofty mission and bring to the German folk that same sense of elevation and dedication with which the works of the Athenian playwrights had once inspired the ancient Greeks. At this time Wagner believed in the innate virtue and noble artistic instincts of the folk; it was the degenerate courtiers who had misled both folk and king and who formed the main stumbling block to his proposals. The elimination of these parasitic aristocrats would bring freedom, and in some vague, romantic, marvelous, and Wagnerian way the Germanic world, redeemed by its theatre, would be a happy land in which monarchy would be eradicated and kinghood simultaneously emancipated. It is not surprising that such nebulous ideas inspired Bakunin, a friend of Marx and Engels, then resident in Dresden, with contempt for Wagner's so-called politics. Like his Lohengrin, Wagner frequently longed to retire from a world which did not comprehend his artistic charge; he sank himself in poetry, the Eddas and sagas.

The spring of 1848 brought hope; revolution in Paris and the expulsion of Louis Philippe had been followed by barricades in Vienna, Berlin, and Prague. A parliament sat in Frankfurt-on-the-Main to frame a constitution for a united Germany. Perhaps, if his ideas were adopted, the folk would soon be free, and the Wagnerian Utopia would rise in Saxony. Wagner did not hesitate to send suggestions to the august body. He optimistically peered into the future, where he perceived the Germans, resembling gods, busy at their task of civilizing the globe. This was not the vision that Heine had seen four years before in his *Deutschland: Ein Winter-maerchen.*

During the summer of 1848 Wagner's cloudy rhetoric reached mystic heights with the writing of *The Wibelungs,* a determined but confusing attempt to organize and clarify his reading and thinking on the Rhenish myths of Siegfried and the hoard and their relationship to German history. It has been remarked earlier that in this essay he explains, at least to this own satisfaction, the meaning of the term "Nibelung." Peremptorial solutions to problems in all fields had become a Wagnerian specialty.

The Wibelungs identifies Frederick Barbarossa as the re-born sun god, Siegfried; the Nibelungen hoard mysteriously ascends, is transmuted in the process of time into the Holy Grail, and becomes the object of the emperor's last journey to the East. Despite the turgid prose, a reader with knowledge of the completed cycle of Wagner's masterworks is thrilled to perceive in this essay what the struggling young genius could himself only dimly apprehend, the unparalleled path that lay before him from *Rhinegold* to *Parsifal,* a road that was to lead from the theft of the treasure in the river's depths to the reunion of spear and grail in the temple of Monsalvat.

Wagner had sketched a drama on Barbarossa but abandoned it in favor of a work on Siegfried; he renounced, so he thought, the historical with its dependence upon interpretation and embraced the mythical whose source is his favorite theme, the noble intuition of the folk. But his Siegfried always remained mixed with his vague and muddled concepts of Barbarossa, the German leader, and universal kingship.

The year 1848 also saw the appearance of Wagner's *The Nibelungen Myth as Scheme for a Drama.* It was an attempt to reduce his impressions of the sagas, Eddas, and compendiums of myths into some manageable and cohesive form of his own; this wide-ranging prose outline or scenario which embraces practically all the substance of the present *Ring* was one practical result of the vague ramblings of *The Wibelungs.* Parts of it, the sections dealing with Siegfried and Brynhild's tragedy, he developed into *Siegfried's Death,* a dramatic poem he intended to set musically and which, in scope, would be practical for realization in any major opera house of his time.

It has already been noted that in *Siegfried's Death* the gods are saved through the hero's deed. The poem reflects Wagner's optimism that the degraded society he deplored might yet be reborn through sacrifice and art—a German art that would turn his countrymen, led astray by the quest for gold and the seductions of French and Jewish pseudo-art, back to the essential greatness and profundity of the German spirit.

Today such cant sounds naïve and very disturbing. Unfortunately there is little doubt concerning the ardor of the royal conductor's prejudices; and there is no doubt that he passionately believed in the theatre as a temple of Germanic art where mystic rites might redeem the erring and exorcise the semitic demons, Meyerbeer and Mendelssohn. And need we ask whose works he imagined should form the Proper and Ordinary of this cleansing ritual? He had found in the Teutonic myth the elements he would consecrate for the new sacrament.

In the thirteenth century an Icelandic scribe, inspired by Snorri Sturluson, had turned to the Eddas, wherein he found material with which to exalt the glories of the high Teutonic days on the Rhine; the result was the *Volsunga Saga*. Now, more than half a millennium later, Wagner, too, plunged into the Eddas and, of course, the *Volsunga Saga* itself. His offering for the redemption of the German folk, *The Nibelung's Ring*, a work whose consummation was more than a quarter of a century in the future, had begun to shape itself within his teeming brain.

Wagner and those who anticipated quick political change had been over-optimistic. The constitutional labors of the Frankfurt parliament were rejected by the government of Saxony; the populace revolted, and the king sought refuge at his fortress of Koenigstein, where he awaited deliverance and the restoration of order by Prussian troops. During several days of civil war Wagner was in the center of revolutionary activity. In any case, he was near the end in Dresden both professionally and economically; the projected premiere of his *Lohengrin* had been cancelled because his loyalty was suspected at court, and his personal follies and extravagances had led him into such extraordinary debt that his flight from the city would have been inevitable within a short time. He had little to lose, and he welcomed the exhilaration of the barricades. The rising failed. By a providential escape to Switzerland he eluded capture, indictment for treason, and a possible death sentence.

In his Swiss refuge Wagner turned out a series of polemic prose works compounded of gibberish, fake erudition, cas-- uistry, barbarism, penetrating observation, and divine intuition. They served to purge his overwrought mind and to prepare it for his great task, a return to the prose scenario, *The Nibelungen Myth as Scheme for a Drama*, the progenitor of *Siegfried's Death*, and its transformation, though with many changes, into a quadripartite dramatic poem which evolved into *The Nibelung's Ring*. This giant cycle he planned to set to music; it would be performed on four separate days under festival conditions in a theatre specially consecrated to it. No opera house he knew of was capable of coping with its complications. The four sections of *The Nibelung's Ring* as we know them today, *The Rhinegold, The Valkyrie, Siegfried,* and *The Twilight of the Gods,* constitute the version of the Volsung and Nibelung tales that the modern world knows best. By 1853 Wagner could read a completed *Ring* poem to his friends.

He was no longer the optimist of 1848. His was a mood of resignation, reinforced by reading Schopenhauer. Louis Napoleon's *coup* of 1851 which established the Second French Empire further deepened his despair of Europe's artistic and political future. In the prose outline of 1848 Brynhild cried out to the gods that their crimes were annulled by the hero's assumption of their guilt and that the ring which had induced misery would be cleansed by the funeral fire. But early in 1851 he penned a new valedictory for Brynhild in which she bade the gods fade away in bliss before the hero's deed, for a blessed redemption through death would end their fears.

Wagner's pessimism had built a most extraordinary bridge. For some time an inner compulsion had been urging him towards this almost mystical synthesis, but he had held back.

From the very beginning his conception of the myths had bound the destiny of gods and Volsungs closely together. From hints and vague allusions in Edda and saga he fashioned a tightly woven relationship between happenings in heaven and on earth. The valkyrie, Brynhild, spanned these two worlds.

It has been suggested earlier that the ethical problem implied in the *Volsunga Saga* fascinated Wagner. But there, of course, the Rhenish dynasty is annihilated while the gods, the authors of the dreadful chain of events that culminate in the calamity, go unpunished. Yet the people from whom the *Volsunga Saga* sprang knew that one day the gods must undergo the *ragna rök*. One thinks of that strangely moving moment in the *Volsunga Saga* when the hero seeks to learn from the dying Fafnir about that final day when the blood of gods and giants shall mix.

But nowhere in the ancient tales is the death of Siegfried (Sigurd) connected with the twilight of the gods. Now, since Wagner, it is difficult to separate them. It is he who made the flames of the hero's funeral pyre rise to ignite Walhall itself. By this union of the *Volsunga Saga* with the prophetic utterances of the *Völuspa* a new and fateful mythology had been created whose great artistic heritage has been stigmatized by disastrous political symbolism drawn from it.

For the infatuation his masterpieces worked on the minds of bigots of his time and, more calamitously, of our century, the Wagner of the prose works must bear much guilt. There, to our pain, he expounds his symbols. But, although the music dramas were born of this intellectual squalor, his dramatic and musical genius purify his mind and enable these works to escape the corruption of his fetid political theorizing and become pure creations on a lofty level.

Wagner eventually changed the title of *Siegfried's Death* to *The Twilight of the Gods;* Brynhild's apocalyptic *scena* underwent many variations before it reached its incomparable ultimate form in which Wagner, at the height of his powers, paints in purely musical terms the majestic ruin of the gods and the emergence of a new order after the cataclysm.

At the end he returned to the hopeful prophecy of the *Völuspa;* his assuaging phrases soar above the wreckage of the world and echo the Wala's promise of the coming of the mighty one and a holy and everlasting peace.

After this finale Wagner remarked to the first Bayreuth audience, "It now rests with you; if you wish it, we shall have an art."

9

During 1857 while Wagner, who had already completed *The Valkyrie*, was at work on *Siegfried*, the young Norwegian dramatist, Henrik Ibsen, also made use of the stuff of the *Volsunga Saga*. He adapted the tragedy of Brynhild and Sigurd for the central situation of his play, *The Vikings at Helgeland*.

Wagner's public was generally ignorant of the transformation he had worked upon the saga; on the other hand, Scandinavian critics at first registered resentment over the way Ibsen varied the old theme.

In his opinion the Teutonic mythical world was unsuitable to the modern stage. He could not call upon music to render the implausible credible and to bathe every phrase in atmosphere. Most of the supernatural elements in the tale he suppressed and thus scaled the *Volsunga Saga* down to the proportions of one of the Icelandic family sagas.

In his play Brynhild is called Hjordis. She was adopted by a warrior who was unaware that it was her father whose life he had taken and whose wealth he had seized. Like Andvari in the saga, the father before his death sang out a curse upon his hoard.

One evening at a drinking-feast attended by Sigurd and his friend Gunnar, proud Hjordis declared that the man who wished to wed her must undertake a mighty feat, the slaying of a fierce bear chained outside her chamber. Sigurd loved her, but her haughtiness made him think his affection unreturned; Gunnar prized Hjordis but shrank from the deed. Altruistic Sigurd put on Gunnar's armor, killed the bear, and entered Hjordis' bedroom where she, somewhat foggy from the feasting, believed him to be Gunnar. She accepted his caresses, but upon retiring Sigurd lay his sword between them. The next morning he carried her to Gunnar, who sailed away with the unsuspecting virago while Sigurd consoled himself by eloping with her gentle foster-sister, Dagny. In the darkness of her room, Hjordis had given Sigurd a golden ring which he in time gave to Dagny.

Years later all the characters involved in the deception met at another banquet. An argument rose between the two women as to whose husband had the greater fame. Unable to endure her foster-sister's vicious taunts, Dagny, who had learned the truth from Sigurd, displayed the ring as proof that Sigurd had done the deed. Then, like Gudrun in the saga, she asked that her boast be forgotten. But Hjordis determined upon either hers or Sigurd's death. Unable to incite Gunnar against him, she killed the hero herself. But before he fell to her arrow, the two had admitted their love. Hjordis hurled herself over a cliff, and in the black clouds that blanketed the sky her young son beheld her in valkyrie armour mounted on a horse hurtling towards Walhall.

The play has its faults; the destruction of a large white bear is hardly a satisfying substitute for the great tasks of the saga, the slaying of Fafnir and the penetration of Hindfell's flames. In these terms, the boldest deed ever seen in Iceland becomes a bit silly. Supernatural or not, if Ibsen had kept the dragon of the saga, Sigurd's celebrity would seem more reasonable. Moreover, it is amusing to observe Kriemhild's magic, by means of which in the saga Sigurd and Gunnar exchanged shapes, reduced by Ibsen to the heroine's confusion induced by intemperance. Another quaint touch is Sigurd's dying revelation that under the influence of King Athelstan of England he had become a Christian and was thus unable to join Hjordis on the valkyrie ride to Walhall.

But despite these failings in the early opus of a genius, the play has tremendous power and contains the germs of future development.

In the haughty and fierce Hjordis, *née* Brynhild, who lost the man she loved and married someone she judged a weakling, the reader may see the ancestress of Hedda Gabler; the latter used pistols rather than valkyrie weapons. Sigurd, that heroic compromiser who played with truth, was one day to become Halvard Solness, the Master Builder, who kissed and then forgot a young girl, significantly named Hilda; she later reentered his life to lead him to a glorious death. His very name contains the word for sun (sol) recalling his origin as a god of light.

Motives from the *Volsunga Saga* run through other Ibsen works. An episode in *Peer Gynt* possesses certain similarities to the wooing of Brynhild. A timid groom, unable to approach his defiant bride, sought the aid of Peer, who boasted that he had the *tarnkappe*. Peer betrayed the poor fellow by carrying the girl off to a high mountain where he enjoyed her love. And who can forget the incomparable death scene of Ase in which Peer conjures up Grani to draw a make-believe sled that conducts his aged mother to heaven?

It was in *The Vikings of Helgeland*, however, that for the first time Ibsen treated the theme that he was later to develop in such plays as *Ghosts* and *The Master Builder*—that the house or life built upon a lie must come to grief. This, after all, is the theme of Wagner's *The Nibelung's Ring*. Ibsen and Wagner, two of the greatest dramatists of the nineteenth century, both found the substance of their message imbedded in the thirteenth century *Volsunga Saga*.

10

To turn from Ibsen's *The Vikings at Helgeland* to William Morris' *Sigurd* is a passage from promise to fulfillment. Just as Hebbel at the height of his powers had in his trilogy, *Die Nibelungen*, garbed the *Nibelungenlied* in his own romantic language, so Morris in *Sigurd* re-created the *Volsunga Saga* in the superb lyric poetry of his maturity.

The translation of the saga in collaboration with Eirikr Magnusson was his training ground for *Sigurd*, and at this point it would be valuable to speak of their literary partnership.

Eirikr Magnusson, an Icelander, settled in England and became one of the most outstanding men in the field of Norse literature. Though he spoke and wrote English meticulously, he wished to ally his talent for straightforward and accurate translation with that of a native Englishman gifted in poetry and by their collaboration to produce fine versions of the Icelandic classics. The hopes of his early literary association with George Powell, a wealthy young Welsh dilettante, remained largely unfulfilled because of Powell's irresolute character.

Fortunately in 1868 Magnusson became acquainted with the English poet, artist, and craftsman, William Morris, and a productive association ensued. Despite the pressing demands of his numerous activities, Morris found time for Icelandic lessons with Magnusson and within three months had mastered the language. Although on his trips to Iceland Morris showed conversational fluency, in working with the classics he was extremely cautious. Together he and Magnusson went over the texts, of which Magnusson analyzed the etymological, grammatical, and syntactical peculiarities. Then Magnusson prepared a literal translation. With this before him and buttressed by his knowledge of the original, Morris wrote his own versions. Thus the learning of the one and the literary skill of the other were combined.

Morris had delighted in Norse tales ever since his Oxford days when Edward Burne-Jones had introduced him to Thorpe's *Northern Mythology*. His contributions to the *Oxford and Cambridge Magazine* revealed a sympathy for Norse material, and even before he met Magnusson, he had read the *Elder Edda* and a few sagas in translation. Magnusson was amazed by his knowledge of the geography and history of Iceland.

Even before starting work with Magnusson, Morris had dabbled at Icelandic and tried his hand at translation. Magnusson entered his life at a time when his interest in Norse material was in crescendo. He was in the midst of his labors on *The Earthly Paradise*, a treasure house of versified romances adapted from Greek, Teutonic, and Celtic sources; of these tales organized around the months of the year the finest is Morris' poetizing of the Icelandic *Laxdaela Saga*, which he called *The Lovers of Gudrun*.

One poem of the cycle, *The Fostering of Aslaug*, is of particular interest in connection with the *Volsunga Saga;* Morris based it upon a summary of the *Ragnar Lodbrok Saga* appearing in Thorpe's *Northern Mythology*, and it anticipates the splendid lyric narration of *Sigurd*. The story tells of

Heimir, who after the death of Brynhild and Sigurd fled with their daughter, Aslaug, whom Brynhild had put in his charge before she left for the Rhine to become Gunnar's queen. To save the child from the machinations of Grimhild, Heimir attempted to carry her to the land of the Huns and the protection of her uncle, Atli. But on the way he was killed by an avaricious couple who coveted his golden ornaments. They kept Aslaug, whom they raised as a scullion. However, the brave viking, Ragnar Lodbrok, appeared and made the beautiful girl his queen. Sigurd's children intrigued Morris, for he also started a narrative poem called *The Wooing of Swanhild*, but only a fragment of it was written.

The first products of his partnership with Magnusson were translations of *The Saga of Gunnlaug* and *Grettir's Saga* (1869). The next year saw the appearance of another joint effort, the first rendering in English of the *Volsunga Saga*, the artistic high point of Morris' Norse studies.

In both 1871 and 1873 Morris journeyed to Iceland where he had the joy of visiting places hallowed by the legends he loved. At the very time that the German Schliemann was laboring to expose the ruins of Troy, this Englishman made a pilgrimage to Iceland, which had become his Greece, and exhorted those of the Teutonic strain to look upon the *Volsunga Saga* as their *Iliad*.

May Morris held *Sigurd* to be the central poem of her father's life; this was the work he desired as his monument. It was the outgrowth of his independent adaptations of Norse material, his linguistic studies with Magnusson, his translation of the *Volsunga Saga*, and the inspiration and poetic insight given him by his travels in Iceland. Because he hewed closely to his beloved *Volsunga Saga* rather than reorganizing its ground plan along the lines of a classical epic, some critics, finding *Sigurd* unusual, judged it incoherent.

He began *Sigurd* in October, 1875, when Wagner was deep in preparation for the first performance of his Nibelung cycle at Bayreuth. And like it, Morris' *Sigurd* sings of fate, of that terrible inevitability which ultimately reveals man's passage through life to be nothing more than the tracing of a pattern woven by norns. Humans and gods are compelled by mighty forces to accomplish destinies against which they struggle in vain. Reidmar (Hredimar) warns the Gods:

Ye have changed the world, and it bindeth with the
     right and the wrong ye have made,
Nor may ye be Gods henceforward save the rightful
     ransom be paid.

There is frequently the mood of the prologue to *The Twilight of the Gods*, where norns recite the wages of immemorial sin and give intimations of gods beyond the gods. Morris writes of

. . . the worlds that come and go
On the nether rim of heaven.

and of

. . . the first Gods' fashioning hands.

Though Morris clings closely to the outline of the tale as handed down in the *Volsunga Saga* except where at the end he adopts the *Nibelungenlied's* conception of Gudrun's revenge, he completely changes its spirit. The violent tones and savage accents of the saga which Wagner could realize in *The Valkyrie* could not be mixed on Morris' refined palette. He softens the ferocity of the characters of the *Volsunga Saga*. His gentle muse transforms its rude heroics into lyric nobility, its rough canvas splashed with violent colors into a variegated tapestry of golden highlights and deep shadows. *Sigurd* breathes the rarefied atmosphere of Tennyson at his best. Morris' poetry flows easily and inevitably, carrying his tale forward at a fleeting pace. *Sigurd* is read not only for its lyric beauty but for the great cumulative effect of its narrative.

It was painful to Morris that his poem was rather indifferently received at its appearance in 1877. One year before, Wagner's tetralogy had been premiered at Bayreuth in the presence of two emperors and a throng of adoring followers who had gathered from all over the world. Although in retrospect this success may have somewhat vexed Morris, his temperament, in any case, was not sympathetic to his German contemporary's genius. To Morris the ideal literary stuff for operatic treatment was Don Giovanni, a most modern-sounding judgment. It is fascinating that as early as 1873, while Wagner was still creating the first act of *The Twilight of the Gods,* a letter of Morris' reveals that he, though far from sympathetically, discerned some of the problems involved in creating and mounting this stupendous drama.

Wagner's concept of *The Nibelung's Ring,* so vast and all-embracing in his early studies, tended to contract when he was confronted with the reality of reducing the titanic action to the dimensions of a stage. Thus, for example, the clash of two entire races opposed in goals and temperament, the giants and the gods, shrank to less than a score of costumed creatures striking attitudes. Morris writes that it was "nothing short of desecration to bring such a tremendous and world-wide subject under the gaslights of an opera: the most rococo and degraded of all forms of art." Morris' tone is hostile towards Wagner and opera, but the problem is stated, and Wagner himself recognized it.

How often did Wagner lament that his chosen art made him dependent upon the intelligence, vocal resources, musicianship, and physical appearance of his interpreters. Morris' dismay at "the idea of a sandy-haired German tenor tweedledeeing over the unspeakable woes of Sigurd" was not really far from Wagner's frequent anguish at performances of his own works.

Accounts of the Bayreuth productions roused Morris' ire. He judged futile and ridiculous the appearance on stage of the dreadful Fafnir in the form of an English pantomime dragon emitting puffs of steam. Most offensive to him seemed the awakening of Brynhild, where the tenor, having pierced the valkyrie's armor only to discover her form still decorously draped, cries aloud, "Das ist kein Mann."

Morris' criticisms have a modern ring, for today the approach to Wagnerian staging leads away from the literalism so dear to this master. Moreover, Morris realized that the Wagnerian *Gesamtkunstwerk,* in which, theoretically, music, drama, and the fine arts were to hold equal sway, was an impossibility and that the poetic, the element most important to him, would emerge subservient to the music.

11

From the material of the *Volsunga Saga*, the Eddic poems, and the *Nibelungenlied*, Wagner and Morris shaped independent works, *The Nibelung's Ring* and *Sigurd* respectively. The slightest suggestion gleaned from a source was sufficient to spur their artistic powers; but in each the creative process worked differently.

In forming *The Nibelung's Ring* Wagner did not restrict himself to the above sources. He ranged widely, devouring Lachmann's publications on the Nibelungen subject, Jacob Grimm's *Deutsche Mythologie*, Wilhelm Grimm's *Deutsche Heldensagen*, and the Hagen-Simrock *Das deutsche Heldenbuch*; his acquaintance with sagas included not only the *Volsunga*, but the *Vilkina* and Snorri's *Heimskringla*.

Certainly Morris' reading was as profound. The point to be stressed in the case of Wagner is that from these many works, bits and pieces of legends accumulated in his febrile brain where they were further fragmented, mixed, transformed, and then reshaped into the completely "new" mythology of his tetralogy. Any attempt to follow his creative path is, of course, hypothetical. Yet it might be helpful to guess at how he fashioned, for example, the main symbol of his drama, the cursed and powerful ring.

In the nineteenth adventure of the *Nibelungenlied* there is a casual reference to a magic wishing-rod lying on the hoard which could make its discoverer master of the world. This alluring bit of information is never put to use by anyone in the tale, but Wagner evidently seized upon it; by combining this rod with the ring cursed by the dwarf in the *Volsunga Saga*, he forged the famous and dreaded ring of the Nibelung, a symbol of unlimited and cursed power which could dominate the universe.

Perhaps as he created the psychologically profound scene in *Siegfried* in which Wotan bars the hero's access to the sleeping Brynhild, there hovered in Wagner's mind remembrance of that moving fragment of old Low-German poetry called the *Hildebrandslied* (*ca.* 800) wherein a conflict to the death is spurred by a hasty and suspicious youth who does not recognize his opponent as his parent. Old Hildebrandt is that same faithful armorer to Dietrich of Bern who in the *Nibelungenlied,* enraged at the slaying of Hagen by a woman's hand, sprang at Kriemhild, slew her, and thus accomplished the end of the Nibelungs. The *Hildebrandslied* pictures him after the calamity in the land of the Huns as he journeys homewards and by chance meets his son. Matthew Arnold tells a similar tale in his noble *Sohrab and Rustum.* So closely interknit are the *Volsunga Saga,* the *Nibelungenlied,* and the *Hildebrandslied,* that it is certain that Wagner also knew this last source, whose material supplements the story of the *Nibelungenlied* just as the tale of Aslaug amplifies a detail of the *Volsunga Saga's* plot.

Even the sweep of the whole Nibelung theme was not sufficiently vast for Wagner. It has been shown how he had the original idea of binding it to the Eddic concept of the *ragna rök.* But this, too, was not enough. From the simple statement of Brynhild in the *Volsunga Saga,* "But . . . I vowed a vow, that never would I wed one who knew the name of fear," Wagner concluded that Sigurd was no one other than the boy of the old story who was too thick-headed to learn the meaning of fear. Wagner's amalgamation of this tale with both the Nibelungen legends and the twilight of the gods was not entirely successful and makes for some labored spots in *Siegfried;* however, it clearly shows Wagner's methods of assembling his plots by what psychologists call "association."

Morris' purposes and methods were completely different. He wished to preserve in his *Sigurd* the story, characters, and ground plan of that work which through his translation had become part of him, the *Volsunga Saga;* true, he tightened its action by suppressing what he considered fruitless digressions and sought to reduce the plethora of gory detail and some of the un-Victorian behavior. Except that like Wagner he turned to the *Nibelungenlied* for the concluding episodes of his poem and introduced some touches from the *Elder Edda,* his literary technique was not the Wagnerian one of joining previously unrelated elements into a new whole; rather his was to embroider poetic passages from the merest hints in his source. Simple statements in the saga such as, "Forth Sigurd rides till he comes," he expands into lyric tapestries of marvelous description. The *Volsunga Saga*, as barren of foliage as a Michelangelo fresco or the rocky terrain of Mantegna and Tura, becomes florescent at this poet's touch; his Sigurd in the region of Hlymdale traverses landscapes of Tennysonian loveliness.

And the dark as well as the light is within Morris' compass. In the *Volsunga Saga* Regin simply states that "there was a dwarf called Andvari, who ever abode in that force." From this, Morris beautifully elaborates:

> There is a desert of dread in the uttermost part of the
> world,
> Where over a wall of mountains is a mighty water
> hurled,
> Whose hidden head none knoweth, nor where it meeteth
> the sea;
> And that force is the Force of Andvari, and an Elf
> of the Dark is he.

Morris used the passage of time and the seasons to frame sections of his tale and to provide yet more opportunities for painting in words. Though by these methods Morris conjures poetry from the tale, his additions are never discordant with its essence.

This remarkable ability to embellish forms without seeming to exhaust their possibilities was also his particular gift in the graphic arts. During his vacation trips in France he had seen the gothic marvels of Rouen, Beauvais, Amiens, and Chartres and had resolved to become an architect. He studied with so famous a master as Street, whose Law Courts still stand on the Strand. But Morris abandoned the field, for he realized that his talent was essentially that of a decorator. Given a structure, he could furnish and enrich it; he could create intricate wallpapers, carpets, hangings, and resonant stained glass. And in none of his many undertakings does this decorative genius shine more brightly than in printing, wherein his private press triumphed with the production of the beautiful and famed Kelmscott Chaucer, a monument to his friendship with Burne-Jones.

It has been shown how in a way quite different from Morris' decorative technique in *Sigurd*, Wagner, the dramatist, assembled the literary structure of *The Nibelung's Ring;* but Wagner, the musician, is a true cousin to William Morris; the musical side of him delights in Morris' kind of romantic descriptive elaboration, and every change in light and every progress of his characters through space he exploits as an opportunity to write program music.

In the prologue to *The Twilight of the Gods*, for example, a magnificent exercise in sevenths and ninths evokes the expanding light of the sun as it falls upon Hindfell; then Brynhild and her hero emerge to sing their duet; she has given him her runic knowledge, and in thanks for it and the gift of her horse, Grani, he bestows upon her the dwarf's ring. Here incidentally are some typical Wagnerian alterations; in the *Volsunga Saga*, Grani is Sigurd's horse selected by Odin; moreover, since Wagner eliminates the scene at Hlymdale, he transfers, to excellent dramatic purpose, the presentation of the ring to this scene on the valkyrie rock as did Morris in *Sigurd*. After the hero departs to work his mighty deeds in Brynhild's name, the orchestra paints a tonal picture of his descent in the full sunshine from the cliff of Hindfell to the valley of the Rhine; his horn call grows fainter as he recedes; the musical motives of nature and the Rhine tell of his river trip, and midst falling shadows he arrives at the capital of the Rhenish kingdom. Thus flanking the love duet are two elaborate musical descriptions, one of change in light and another combining change of light with motion through space.

Of course, Wagner's genius makes these sections reinforce the over-all picture. Though it would be hard to imagine the score without them, yet the plot, as distinct from the total dramatic impression, would in no way be imperiled were they suppressed. In fact, they are frequently ripped from context and played as independent pieces in the concert hall.

The Nibelung's Ring has many other similar examples. The comings and goings of the gods and the troubled weather conditions of *The Rhinegold* provide Wagner with unparalleled opportunities for the portrayal of light and space through sound.

Though it may be argued that such programmatic tone-poems often serve the practical purpose of filling space and covering the sound of scene-changes—an almost sacrilegious observation about so much magnificent music—one need only glance at *Lohengrin* for reassurance that such methods were part of the inner construction of Wagner's art. For in that opera, with no change of scene involved, the profound action of the second act struggles to assert itself between heraldic processions. From the beginning there was in Wagner constant contention between the deep, taut philosophical drama he carved out of the ancient truths of legends such as the *Volsunga Saga* and the grand opera he had learned from Meyerbeer, a tradition that insisted upon the musical elaboration of set pieces which even in Wagner's hands remain just that, no matter how artfully he imbeds them in the tissue of his drama. Only *Tristan*, an exception to every rule, escapes the dilemma. With no slight to the penetration of Wagner's dramatic recitative and arioso and his brilliant psychological use of motifs, it is to be observed that pure musical decoration plays a substantial part in his works. Though, like the *Volsunga Saga*, Wagner's book for *The Nibelung's Ring* is stark, his romantic decorations, like Morris', are often picturesque and ornamentative.

12

As young men both Wagner and Morris showed great diversity of talent. It was characteristic of men of the romantic century to strive for versatility of expression. Berlioz, like Wagner, wrote the book of an operatic cycle which he set to music and was, moreover, a critic admired for his style. Schumann turned out verse, novels, and plays, and during his pathetically brief musical career his literary artistry made the *Zeitschrift für Musik*, which he founded, a highly influential publication. Many abilities strove for precedence within Wagner, dramatic, poetic, musical, and in addition his dilettantish essays at philosophic, aesthetic, political, and economic theorizing. Morris was poet, painter, architect, decorator, and social reformer.

This desire for achievement in many fields was but one aspect of the romantic ambition to break down the boundaries between the various arts in order to effect an amalgamation of many expressions within a single form; the fugitive archetype of that form was the *Gesamtkunstwerk,* the all-embracing art work. In the case of Wagner this elusive concept became the object of a life-long quest. In the field of decorative printing Morris sought a more modest synthesis of labors in literature, art, handicrafts, and medieval research.

The lure of the medieval was great for both Wagner and Morris. Wagner turned to Gottfried von Strassburg and Wolfram von Eschenbach; Morris to Froissart and Malory. But the medievalism of each sprang from different sources and had dissimilar purposes and traits. Wagner's atmospheric medievalism was fathered by the unrealities of E.T.A. Hoffmann; Morris' more substantial medievalism was born of the earnest gothic revival of Pugin and Ruskin and partakes of the solemnity of the Oxford Movement.

Hoffmann was one of those multi-faceted early romantics. He was an official of the Prussian government, an artist, a composer whose opera *Undine* is a monument of historic importance, and, above all, the author of eerie and daemonic tales. Unfortunately most English-speaking people know him, if at all, only as the besotted hero of Offenbach's opera.

The neurotic gothic spirit epitomized by Hoffmann is paralleled by the appearance in the concert halls of Europe of the Genoese Paganini, the weird and mysterious virtuoso whose fantastic technique and ability to spellbind an audience were rumored to have been bought at the price of his soul. Similar in spirit are the creations of Berlioz, his symphony with its march to the scaffold and witches' sabbath, and its strange sequel, *Lélio.*

Hoffmann's tales had filled the young Wagner with a feverish excitement that provoked visions. The boy even tried his hand at writing Hoffmannesque stories. It was music's narcotic effect rather than music itself which most interested him as a young man. And to the end of his career

Wagner looked upon music as a kind of magic; he was a Prospero with book and wand who sought rule over a world of inferior spirits. His aim was to sway the senses and thus to captivate, subdue, and lecture an audience rendered unquestioning. Like his Lohengrin, whose motto was "Never interrogate me," Wagner preferred that his artistic and personal origins be veiled in mystery. His famous letter to Hans von Bülow shows how angered he became if the influences that formed his musical style were discussed in public. "Lay aside your doubts," Lohengrin tells Elsa as she seeks to discover whence her attractive but mysterious lover came, "My origins lie in radiance and ecstasy."

Wagner was a child of the magic, painted-cardboard gothic, best represented on the German stage of his youth by a scene in von Weber's *Der Freischütz,* where in a deep ravine of the Bohemian forest magic bullets are cast with the devil's help. Although he built his foundations deeper, Wagner's gothic was that of Beckford's and Wyatt's ill-fated Fonthill Abbey; Morris' was more akin to Pugin's Scarisbrick Hall.

Wagner's naïveté in matters of medieval history, his extraordinary ego, or both are exemplified by his remark that in *Lohengrin* he had painted a complete picture of the middle ages! This absurdity was topped by his wife and high-priestess, Cosima, who added that *Lohengrin* was the one and only monument of that era!

Morris' serious medievalism influenced all his work, artistic, poetic, and political. His cautious and scholarly approach to his manifold talents bears resemblance to the universality of Goethe. At this point it would be suitable to turn to the elements that contributed to Morris' unity and integrity of vision.

13

Morris' England revaluated medieval times. Victorians lived in a disjointed world fractured by the Industrial Revolution; the machine flourished as the hand trades sank and taste declined. Labor, more and more divided, toiled in misery, and higher and more impenetrable barriers rose between classes. Troubled by what they saw, intellectuals turned to study the unified structure of medieval society where, ideally, class was answerable to class, and each man had his place.

At times this medievalism was romantic and nostalgic; out of a past that time had clothed in enchantment were glimpsed appealing images, great cathedrals and monasteries rising on landscapes as yet unscarred by industry, honest workers united in fraternal guilds, unhurried sculptors devoting their utmost skill to the carving of a saint. But to many these were more than evocative pictures; they furnished patterns and traditions to be turned to the salvation of an evil present.

The moral power of the medieval guild to regulate labor conditions as well as the quality and distribution of goods was contrasted with the unrestricted free trade of nineteenth century *laissez faire;* the fortune of the medieval poor, tended by the charity of almshouse and cathedral chapter, with the scarcely bearable near serfdom of the Lancashire mill worker; the beauty of medieval handicraft with machine ugliness.

Men like Southey, Carlyle, Ruskin, Pugin, and Morris, each in his own way, contemplated the medieval scene and found lessons to be learned; medievalism became associated with the important social, artistic, and religious questions of the day—the guilds reborn, as was supposed, in the trade union movement, gothic forms in architecture revived by Pugin and in painting and poetry by the Pre-Raphaelites, the retrospective liturgical reform by the Oxford Movement and the Ecclesiologists.

In contrast to dismembered Victorian society the middle ages offered the image of a spiritually unified community, the vision of a kind of social and political *Gesamtkunstwerk* where each element contributed its part to the whole.

Yet Morris had a not uncritical attitude towards the middle ages. He realized that much idealized medievalism resulted from the oversimplification of some facts and the ignoring of others, and he recognized the crude, tyrannical, and barbarous aspects of that age. But he rejoiced in its forthrightness and vigor, the antipodes to Victorian hypocrisy, and especially valued these qualities in the *Volsunga Saga.*

With Ruskin the reform movement took up an increasingly anti-industrial theme which Morris developed. Yet, although *The Stones of Venice,* published during Morris' first year at Oxford, had great influence upon him, he rejected Ruskin's idea that inequality was just and inevitable, and he eventually sought the spiritual reintegration of society through socialism. Like Ruskin, Morris the artist, realizing that art is the bloom of a particular culture, entered politics in order to attempt a cure for the failing plant by healing the diseased root.

Morris' medievalism and his socialism became bound together; he always found an example from the one to inspire hope for the other. His *Sigurd* of 1876 is filled with indications of his coming espousal of the socialistic cause. A defender of the poor, his golden hero's victories advance social equality. In Morris' hands Sigurd of the *Volsunga Saga* became a reformer. Sigurd says in his famous speech to Giuki:

> And I would that the loving were loved, and I would that the weary should sleep,
> And that man should hearken to man, and that he that soweth should reap.

His benevolence becomes renowned.

> And they sing of the golden Sigurd and the face without a foe,
> And the lowly man exalted and the mighty brought alow:
> And they say, when the sun of the summer shall come aback to the land,
> It shall shine on the fields of the tiller that fears no heavy hand;
> That the sheaf shall be for the plougher, and the loaf for him that sowed,
> Through every furrowed acre where the Son of Sigmund rode.

Bringing peace to the righteous, he pursued the unregenerate with war and was not unlike a militant Balder, bringing a new age after the *ragna rök*. Indeed, in this poem and in other writings Morris frequently implies that the world must undergo some kind of dissolution, violent if necessary, before

the Utopia shall be founded; the concept of the calamity
brings forth some great passages in *Sigurd;* but, unlike in
Wagner, there is no direct connection between it and the
hero's death.

On that day unborn in the darkness, the last of all
    earthly days,
The last of the days of battle, when the host of the Gods
    is arrayed
And there is an end forever of all who were once afraid.

The *ragna rök* became symbolic to Morris of a great and
inevitable truth. It was his hope and religion at a period when
his contemporary, Wagner, was turning to a less strenuous
theory of redemption through inner spiritual development
as expounded in his mysterious and magnificent *Parsifal.*
Wagner was out of the combat; as indicated in his *The
Wibelungs* of three decades before *Parsifal,* Andvari's gold,
sought by the Frankish kings, had mysteriously ascended and
become the Holy Grail.

A case for including the pre-*Parsifal* Wagner among the
great nineteenth century artist-socialists, a group that includes not only Morris but also his spiritual mentor, Ruskin,
and his close friend, Shaw, has been made by the latter in
The Perfect Wagnerite. To Shaw the gigantic apparatus of
The Nibelung's Ring is an allegory of socialism; the depths
of Nibelheim are the smoky Manchesters of the world where
the Nibelungs, the spiritually disenfranchised workers, toil
miserably for Alberich, whose *Tarnkappe,* possessing the
power of rendering him present but invisible, is a striking
symbol of the corporate stockholder. Wagner adopted a tradition mentioned in Snorri's *Younger Edda* that the dwarf's
ring was capable of breeding more gold, and to Shaw it
becomes a symbol of that heartless power that enslaves.

Shaw develops the allegory with great ingenuity, and there
are elements in it that may even have occurred to Wagner.
But on the whole it is difficult to reconcile with an artist like
Wagner who, though he detested the concepts of industrialism
and private property (especially when the property did not
belong to him), really had a basic philosophy of personal

opportunism camouflaged by vague ramblings about universal kingship and the superman, a concept common to Carlyle, Shaw, and Nietzsche.

For Shaw the social significance of *The Nibelung's Ring* ends with the second act of *Siegfried*. He rejects as nothing but opera the awakening of Brynhild and all of *The Twilight of the Gods*. This disapproval, supported by debatable arguments, also involves a disparagement of Wagner's unique handling of the *ragna rök*, scornfully dismissed by Shaw as an adequate answer to the childish question of what becomes of Wotan. *The Perfect Wagnerite*, as its title tells us, is really about its brilliant author.

Of course echoes of Marxian ideas and phraseology can be detected in Wagner's writing, and it is certainly possible that he had read the *Communist Manifesto*, which appeared at the time of the revolutionary movement in Dresden. Yet his claim to be a "communist" in the context of Proudhon, whom he had read, and Bakunin, whom he befriended, is to be taken no more seriously than Ruskin's similar avowal. Wagner's socialism was but one of many poses struck by a theatrical genius.

Quite the opposite was Morris' unfeigned devotion to this cause. In the welter of socialistic hypotheses Morris sought a personal postulation of a *Gesamtkunstwerk* of life derived from the gothic middle ages, a theoretical creation that embraced all of man's efforts, political, ethical, and artistic. Man was to find his place in a society newly integrated on a basis of responsibility and equality, a significant change from the medieval concept of responsibility and hierarchy. It was the integrality of life in the middle ages that most attracted Morris. To the achievement of this fugitive goal he dedicated his remaining years.

While Wagner attempted to unite the arts into a superform, the contemplation of which was to ennoble the spectator, Morris strove to harmonize the labors of existence into a masterwork of joyful living of which art would be the noble reflection. For Wagner life was to gain meaning through a great, i.e. Wagnerian, art; for Morris great art was to mirror a good life.

One need not agree with his attitudes to realize that, unlike Wagner's highly personal philosophy, which had meaning only as long as his works were held to be the *non plus ultra* of all art, Morris' artistic and social theories still have meaning for many. A modest man, he would be astounded and certainly pleased could he read the many histories of art that now hail him as the father of the modern movement and one of the towering influences on this century. As a man he was not unlike his famous contemporary, Leo Tolstoy; for both, though born to wealth and ease, were yet so sensitive to the misery in the world that their personal fortunes became offensive to them and they directed their labors towards achieving social equality.

The *Volsunga Saga,* a product of the middle ages whose roots were fed by the Teutonic heroic age, fascinated Morris and Wagner because of its national origins as well as for reasons of its era and structure. Morris was a Germanophile who ascribed the best qualities of his countrymen to their Teutonic strain inherited from the Anglo-Saxons. Indeed, he somewhat regretted the Roman Occupation and Norman Conquest as having made impossible the development of a nation of mixed Celts and Germans. Wagner's glorification of the Germans is axiomatic though he cursed as often as he praised them.

He and Morris mined deep in the Teutonic *Volsunga Saga,* and from its ore fashioned strongly contrasting works. Morris hinted at that world he longed for in which the lowly sower, led by a noble superman, might reap a balanced harvest of goods and spirit. Wagner wallowed in a proto-Freudian feast of sin and punishment; but he overexpanded the limits of the tale in a magnificent additive conception which he never had poetic power enough to realize completely. The totality of his plan can only be grasped by studying his cancelled draughts, discarded plans, and the elusive commentary of his prose works. Compared with the more modest but clearly apprehended frame of *Sigurd,* his *Ring* is, as a literary work, fragmentary and confused.

But Wagner's score, that glorious patchwork of over a quarter-century of musical evolution, is able to give even the most difficult parts of his text the semblance of substance. His methods of achieving this prodigy will be examined in the following section, which treats the manner in which he and also Morris deepened the psychology of the *Volsunga Saga*.

14

That the author of the *Volsunga Saga* had a most profound insight into human psychology is best revealed in the scene in which Sigurd and Brynhild confront one another after her quarrel with Gudrun and the fraud it unmasked. With an economy of words their souls are sounded as, for example, in Sigurd's simple justification of his conduct, "And withal and in spite of all I was well content that we were all together." In Morris' poem the characters not only feel as deeply as their prototypes, but as children of the romantic movement are more sensitive and articulate, speaking their joys and woes unreservedly in a musical rhymed hexameter with a soft and flexible medial caesura.

In Wagner's hands the characters also become more eloquent and even more impassioned. But their talk, expressed in the alliterative verse of venerable Teutonic *Stabreim*, one of the leading poetic characteristics of the ancient Eddic lays, tends toward recapitulative narration or the simple presentation of a situation. For his masterful projection of psychological subtleties and to achieve his great lyric flow of emotion Wagner relied upon music.

He could never express himself completely in either poetry or in the symphonic forms of absolute music; his particular genius spoke fully only through that hybrid combination of both called the opera. Although occasionally he could pen passages of genuine beauty, in general Wagner's poetic talent was seldom more than sufficient to versify his excellent libretti, which demonstrate extraordinary psychological perception and a talent for setting up striking dramatic situations. The great lyric beauty of his works inheres mainly in the music which clothes the whole and renders it greater than the sum of its parts. He believed that the orchestra should assume that role of commentator on the action once played in the ancient Greek drama by the chorus.

Thus that deeper psychology that Morris could manifest in words, Wagner achieved through music, through leitmotifs

—themes which in a most flexible way represent personages of the drama, objects, situations, and recurrent ideas. By transforming these motifs in respect to color, contour, and rhythm as the dramatic situation demanded and by presenting them alone, fragmented, or woven together in various combinations as part of his orchestral tissue, Wagner by a process of association could recollect, reflect, or anticipate the elation or agitation of his characters, could speak their unspoken thoughts, or even communicate to the audience information of which those on stage were unaware. Of course, all of this musical working out not only mirrored the drama but also proceded according to logical musical form.

In their works both men struggled to give adequate expression to the climax, which in *Sigurd* as in the *Volsunga Saga* is found at the confrontation of Sigurd and Brynhild after the secret of her betrayal has escaped. Wagner, as has been noted, had married the *Volsunga Saga* to the tale of the *ragna rök*, and this scene of ruin became the goal towards which his gigantic drama traveled. In a most striking parallel to Morris, passages of great beauty created to cap these high points were mysteriously suppressed.

Possibly Morris sought emotional release for himself by writing the deeply felt lines in which the lovers turn from misfortune to recall their first meeting on Hindfell and the promise of young love.

> Far fore-seeing we were and wise of many things,
> Of the deeds we twain should accomplish . . .
> But we saw not the sundering hour and the edge of the
> Niblung sword.

She laments,

> O sorrow, sorrow, and sorrow that the world lives after
> the lie! . . .
> But indeed for the death were we fashioned, we meet
> in the death alone,
> We the Son and Daughter of Odin and the flower of his
> longing grown.

For reasons which will never be entirely clear Morris struck out this section, one of his finest poetic utterances.

Wagner's long quest for a finale to *The Nibelung's Ring* has already been described. Although in 1876 as a special favor to King Ludwig of Bavaria he set to music his early ending of *The Twilight of the Gods,* which begins with the splendid "Verging wie Hauch der Goetter Geschlecht," a passage which Shaw scoffs at as "a homily on the efficacy of the Love panacea," it was understood that the setting would never be incorporated into any performance. Wagner's final revision presents a much more neutral text with the poetic message devolving upon his eloquent orchestra.

The characters of the *Volsunga Saga* and their adventures at times recall an animated frieze on which well defined but somewhat stiff figures are for the most part modeled in profile while here and there a head, cut almost in the round, thrusts itself forward as though in an effort to escape the confining surface. Morris and Wagner, each with his own technique, undercut deeply to free these heroic people from the stone; added dimensions of sentiment and sensuousness are gained through entirely different mediums.

15

Morris and Magnusson inserted strophes from the Eddic poems into the prose of their *Volsunga Saga* translation. They had a good precedent for this procedure in the practice of the sagaman himself who imbedded in his tale verses, some of which can be traced back to the *Elder Edda,* the others representing the only surviving fragments of Eddic poems that have otherwise disappeared. The sagaman not only drew upon a more complete version of the *Elder Edda* than has come down to us but also upon an oral tradition still vital.

The snippet of verse that describes Sigmund and Sinfjotli sawing their way out of the burial mound in which Siggeir imprisoned them is certainly the remnant of a longer poem. Also the excellent lines beginning with, "The flame flared at its maddest," indicate that at one time there existed an excellent poem on the wooing of Brynhild. The fragment beginning with, "The worm Sigurd slew," as well as the hyperbolical verses describing the hero's distress on leaving

Brynhild's presence both probably come from a *Long Lay of Sigurd* of which only a part survives. In these remaining stanzas and in the fragments of the *Lay of Brynhild* can be found the recipe the sagaman quotes for making Guttorm fierce enough to kill Sigurd—"Fish of the wild-wood, worm smooth crawling."

The verses that Loki and Andvari exchange, Loki's song of warning to Hreidmar, and Hnikar's poem begging Sigurd to take him aboard his ship are all taken from the Eddic *Lay of Regin.* Similarly the sagaman inserted Brynhild's runic counsel from the *Lay of Sigrdrifa.* The poetic picture of the men who journeyed after Gudrun to Alf's court and the description of the dreadful drink given her come from the *Second Lay of Gudrun.* The racy lines of Hamdir, "Off were the head if Erp were alive yet," can be traced to the *Lay of Hamdir.*

To these poetic gleanings by the sagaman Morris and Magnusson added even more extensive Eddic quotations: Hnikar's advice to Sigurd from the *Lay of Regin,* the songs of the birds from the *Lay of Fafnir,* the great awakening stanzas of the valkyrie from the *Lay of Sigrdrifa,* and the elegiac *First Lay of Gudrun,* which the translators inserted after Sigurd's slaying. The last mentioned poem, a self-contained work of great emotional power, cast its long shadow upon the seventeenth adventure of the *Nibelungenlied,* wherein Kriemhild buries and grieves over her husband.

The translators end the tale with a sentence culled from Snorri's *Younger Edda* followed by the final stanza of the Eddic *Whetting of Gudrun.* This contrived epilogue they obviously modeled after the final stanza of the *Nibelungenlied.*

Much of the poetry of the *Elder Edda* relevant to the *Volsunga Saga* is presented by Morris and Magnusson in a second section of their translation. Thus we are given a metrical parallel to a good part of the story. In addition they could not resist including two extremely beautiful Eddic poems whose relationship to the *Volsunga Saga* is really only tangential. One poem, part of a *Lay of Helgi* (that son of Sigmund who disappears from the action early in the *Volsunga Saga*), describes how Sigrun cursed her brother Dag for slaying her husband Helgi; it includes the famous metaphor likening Helgi to the ash-tree and the dew-sprinkled fawn; so great was Gudrun's grief that it summoned his bleeding spirit back from Walhall to his burial mound, which she entered to visit and lie with him. This work is one of the glories of Norse poetry.

The second poem added by Morris and Magnusson is the *Lament of Oddrun,* which concerns the prophecy in the *Volsunga Saga* uttered by Brynhild before her suicide. This speech is derived from the Eddic *Short Lay of Sigurd.* She predicted that Gudrun would marry Atli, who in turn would oppose the union of his sister Oddrun to Brynhild's widower, Gunnar, that Atli would surprise these lovers at a tryst and then in revenge would work the destruction of the Giukung princes. Thus to Atli's greed was added the motif of sibling jealousy. This is the version of the Giukung fall, one not completely abandoned by the author of the *Volsunga Saga,* that is developed in the Oddrun poem. Here Gunnar's eloquent harping in the worm pit is a call to Oddrun.

It has been remarked that in the labor of translating the *Volsunga Saga* and the poems of The *Elder Edda,* the creative task of poetizing was Morris' while his colleague, Magnusson, advised on syntactical problems; Magnusson was the grammar, Morris the spirit.

The work offered many challenges. The expression, especially in the lays, is at times so compressed that it does not submit easily to the translator. Moreover, on occasion, as during Brynhild's runic lectures to Sigurd, Morris attempts to render complicated aggregations of kennings—those circumlocutory phrases that seek to call something by anything but its most usual name—in too literal a manner with some strange results:

> Sea-runes good at need,
> Learnt for ship's saving,
> For the good health of the swimming horse.

But these are minor flaws in a magnificent performance. Fondness for figures of speech was excessive in old Norse, and in extreme cases one needs a key to interpret the metaphors; Snorri's *Edda* serves such a purpose. To avoid obscurity some translators ignore these rhetorical embellishments; in the above quotation Morris met them head on.

Morris' translation has been criticized for indulging in too weighty a vocabulary. Yet a poet should not be taken to task for speaking the language of his time. The *Volsunga Saga* is not merely a prose narrative; it is, although unversified, as much poetry in its way as the Eddic lays. The translation of any poetic work is the task of none but a poet; it is his obligation to replace the lyric genius of the original with some poetic inspiration of his own. For if in the passage from one language to another the poem emerges without poetry, what indeed remains? In the case of Milton's or Goethe's epics, where the narrative is often but a skeleton that bears the flesh and blood and poetic invention, the reader would be left with barren bones; even though the case of the *Volsunga Saga* is somewhat different in that the story is of sufficient interest to sustain even a most plain translation, yet is not English literature all the richer that Morris was able both to project the precipitate narrative and at the same time to clothe it in poetry. Mere fragments of this tale occasion the pure poetry of the Eddic songs; here only a translator of creative power avails, and Morris has rendered them in masterful phrases, dark and sumptuous.

His language, rich and varied, was Victorian, of an age that in general admired the opulent, the intricate, and the ornate, as witness the great creations in architecture of Pugin and the full-voiced diapason of Ruskin's almost Biblical prose. Is Morris to be reproved because he spoke in the accents of his era? The forms he chose accord with the subject matter; the archaisms he introduced help achieve tone. The old Norse poets sought atmosphere by the very same means; it is interesting to observe in the ancient skaldic lays the use of already obsolete words.

To read Morris' translation is a poetic experience, and this is its ultimate test.

Acknowledgments

The editor wishes to thank those who have generously aided him, his colleague of Bayreuth, Mr. Max Friedlander, and Mr. Ted Hart, to whom an especial debt of gratitude is owed for help in every aspect of the manuscript's preparation.

VOLSUNGA SAGA

The Story of the Volsungs and Nibelungs

A Prologue in Verse

O HEARKEN, ye who speak the English Tongue,
  How in a waste land ages long ago,
The very heart of the North bloomed into song
  After long brooding o'er this tale of woe!
  Hearken, and marvel how it might be so,
That such a sweetness so well crowned could be
Betwixt the ice-hills and the cold grey sea.

Or rather marvel not, that those should cling
  Unto the thoughts of great lives passed away,
Whom God has stripped so bare of everything,
  Save the one longing to wear through their day,
  In fearless wise; the hope the Gods to stay,
When at that last tide gathered wrong and hate
Shall meet blind yearning on the Fields of Fate.

Yea, in the first grey dawning of our race,
  This ruth-crowned tangle to sad hearts was dear.
Then rose a seeming sun, the lift gave place
  Unto a seeming heaven, far off, but clear;
  But that passed too, and afternoon is here;
Nor was the morn so fruitful or so long
But we may hearken when ghosts moan of wrong.
For as amid the clatter of the town
  When eve comes on with unabated noise,
The soaring wind will sometimes drop adown
  And bear unto our chamber the sweet voice

Of bells that 'mid the swallows do rejoice,
Half-heard, to make us sad, so we awhile
With echoed grief life's dull pain may beguile.

Naught vague, naught base our tale, that seems to
    say,—
  'Be wide-eyed, kind; curse not the hand that smites;
Curse not the kindness of a past good day,
  Or hope of love; cast by all earth's delights,
  For very love: through weary days and nights,
Abide thou, striving howsoe'er in vain,
The inmost love of one more heart to gain!'

So draw ye round and hearken, English Folk,
  Unto the best tale pity ever wrought!
Of how from dark to dark bright Sigurd broke,
  Of Brynhild's glorious soul with love distraught,
  Of Gudrun's weary wandering unto naught,
Of utter love defeated utterly,
Of grief too strong to give Love time to die!

                         WILLIAM MORRIS.

THE STORY OF

THE VOLSUNGS AND NIBELUNGS

Chapter 1

Of Sigi, the Son of Odin

HERE BEGINS the tale, and tells of a man who was named Sigi, and called of men the son of Odin; another man withal is told of in the tale, hight Skadi, a great man and mighty of his hands; yet was Sigi the mightier and the higher of kin, according to the speech of men of that time. Now Skadi had a thrall with whom the story must deal somewhat, Bredi by name, who was called after that work which he had to do; in prowess and might of hand he was equal to men who were held more worthy, yea, and better than some thereof.

Now it is to be told that, on a time, Sigi fared to the hunting of the deer, and the thrall with him; and they hunted deer day-long till the evening; and when they gathered together their prey in the evening, lo, greater and more by far was that which Bredi had slain than Sigi's prey; and this thing he much misliked, and he said that great wonder it was that a very thrall should out-do him in the hunting of deer: so he fell on him and slew him, and buried the body of him thereafter in a snow-drift.

Then he went home at evening tide and says that Bredi had ridden away from him into the wild-wood. "Soon was he out of my sight," he says, "and naught more I wot of him."

Skadi misdoubted the tale of Sigi, and deemed that this was a guile of his, and that he would have slain Bredi. So he sent men to seek for him, and to such an end came their seeking, that they found him in a certain snow-drift; then said Skadi, that men should call that snow-drift Bredi's Drift from henceforth; and thereafter have folk followed, so that in such wise they call every drift that is right great.

Thus it is well seen that Sigi has slain the thrall and murdered him; so he is given forth to be a wolf in holy places, and may no more abide in the land with his father; therewith Odin bare him fellowship from the land, so long a way, that right long it was, and made no stay till he brought him to certain war-ships. So Sigi falls to lying out a-warring with the strength that his father gave him or ever they parted; and happy was he in his warring, and ever prevailed, till he brought it about that he won by his wars land and lordship at the last; and thereupon he took to him a noble wife, and became a great and mighty king, and ruled over the land of the Huns, and was the greatest of warriors. He had a son by his wife, who was called Rerir, who grew up in his father's house, and soon became great of growth, and shapely.

Chapter 2

Of the Birth of Volsung, the Son of Rerir, who was the Son of Sigi

Now SIGI grew old, and had many to envy him, so that at last those turned against him whom he trusted most; yea, even the brothers of his wife; for these fell on him at his unwariest, when there were few with him to withstand them, and brought so many against him, that they prevailed against him, and there fell Sigi and all his folk with him. But Rerir, his son, was not in this trouble, and he brought together so mighty a strength of his friends and the great men of the land, that he got to himself both the lands and kingdom of Sigi his father; and so now, when he deems that the feet under him stand firm in his rule, then he calls to mind that which he had against his mother's brothers, who had slain his father. So the king gathers together a mighty army, and therewith falls on his kinsmen, deeming that if he made their kinship of small account, yet none the less they had first wrought evil against him. So he wrought his will herein, in that he departed not from strife before he had slain all his father's banesmen, though dreadful the deed seemed in every wise. So now he gets land, lordship, and fee, and is become a mightier man than his father before him.

Much wealth won in war gat Rerir to himself, and wedded a wife withal, such as he deemed meet for him, and long they lived together, but had no child to take the heritage after them;

and ill-content they both were with that, and prayed the Gods with heart and soul that they might get them a child. And so it is said that Odin hears their prayer, and Freyia no less hearkens wherewith they prayed unto her: so she, never lacking for all good counsel, calls to her her casket-bearing may, the daughter of Hrimnir the giant, and sets an apple in her hand, and bids her bring it to the king. She took the apple, and did on her the gear of a crow, and went flying till she came whereas the king sat on a mound, and there she let the apple fall into the lap of the king; but he took the apple and deemed he knew whereto it would avail; so he goes home from the mound to his own folk, and came to the queen, and some deal of that apple she ate.

So, as the tale tells, the queen soon knew that she was big with child, but a long time wore or ever she might give birth to the child: so it befell that the king must needs go to the wars, after the custom of kings, that he may keep his own land in peace: and in this journey it came to pass that Rerir fell sick and got his death, being minded to go home to Odin, a thing much desired of many folk in those days.

Now no otherwise it goes with the queen's sickness than heretofore, nor may she be the lighter of her child, and six winters wore away with the sickness still heavy on her; so that at the last she feels that she may not live long; wherefore now she bade cut the child from out of her; and it was done even as she bade; a man-child was it, and great of growth from his birth, as might well be; and they say that the youngling kissed his mother or ever she died; but to him is a name given, and he is called Volsung; and he was king over Hunland in the room of his father. From his early years he was big and strong, and full of daring in all manly deeds and trials, and he became the greatest of warriors, and of good hap in all the battles of his warfaring.

Now when he was fully come to man's estate, Hrimnir the giant sends to him Ljod his daughter; she of whom the tale told, that she brought the apple to Rerir, Volsung's father. So Volsung weds her withal; and long they abode together with good hap and great love. They had ten sons and one daughter, and their eldest son was hight Sigmund, and their daughter Signy; and these two were twins, and in all wise the foremost and the fairest of the children of Volsung the king, and mighty, as all his seed was; even as has been long told from ancient days, and in tales of long ago, with the greatest fame of all men, how that the Volsungs have been great men and high-minded and far above the most of men both in cunning and in prowess and all things high and mighty.

So says the story that king Volsung let build a noble hall in such a wise, that a big oak-tree stood therein, and that the limbs of the tree blossomed fair out over the roof of the hall, while below stood the trunk within it, and the said trunk did men call Branstock.

Chapter 3

Of the Sword that Sigmund, Volsung's Son, drew from the Branstock

THERE WAS a king called Siggeir, who ruled over Gothland, a mighty king and of many folk; he went to meet Volsung, the king, and prayed him for Signy his daughter to wife; and the king took his talk well, and his sons withal, but she was loth thereto, yet she bade her father rule in this as in all other things that concerned her; so the king took such rede that he gave her to him, and she was bethrothed to King Siggeir; and for the fulfilling of the feast and the wedding, was King Siggeir to come to the house of King Volsung. The king got ready the feast according to his best might, and when all things were ready, came the king's guests and King Siggeir withal at the day appointed, and many a man of great account had Siggeir with him.

The tale tells that great fires were made endlong the hall, and the great tree aforesaid stood midmost thereof; withal folk say that, whenas men sat by the fires in the evening, a certain man came into the hall unknown of aspect to all men; and suchlike array he had, that over him was a spotted cloak, and he was bare-foot, and had linen-breeches knit tight even unto the bone, and he had a sword in his hand as he went up to the Branstock, and a slouched hat upon his head: huge he was, and seeming-ancient, and one-eyed. So he drew his sword and

93

smote it into the tree-trunk so that it sank in up to the hilts; and all held back from greeting the man. Then he took up the word, and said—

"Whoso draweth this sword from this stock, shall have the same as a gift from me, and shall find in good sooth that never bare he better sword in hand than is this."

Therewith out went the old man from the hall, and none knew who he was or whither he went.

Now men stand up, and none would fain be the last to lay hand to the sword, for they deemed that he would have the best of it who might first touch it; so all the noblest went thereto first, and then the others, one after other; but none who came thereto might avail to pull it out, for in nowise would it come away howsoever they tugged at it; but now up comes Sigmund, King Volsung's son, and sets hand to the sword, and pulls it from the stock, even as if it lay loose before him; so good that weapon seemed to all, that none thought he had seen such a sword before, and Siggeir would fain buy it of him at thrice its weight of gold, but Sigmund said—

"Thou mightest have taken the sword no less than I from there whereas it stood, if it had been thy lot to bear it; but now, since it has first of all fallen into my hand, never shalt thou have it, though thou biddest therefor all the gold thou hast."

King Siggeir grew wroth at these words, and deemed Sigmund had answered him scornfully, but whereas he was a wary man and a double-dealing, he made as if he heeded this matter in nowise, yet that same evening he thought how he might reward it, as was well seen afterwards.

Chapter 4

How King Siggeir wedded Signy, and bade King Volsung and his Son to Gothland

Now IT IS to be told that Siggeir goes to bed by Signy that night, and the next morning the weather was fair; then says King Siggeir that he will not bide, lest the wind should wax, or the sea grow impassible; nor is it said that Volsung or his sons letted him herein, and that the less, because they saw that he was fain to get him gone from the feast. But now says Signy to her father—

"I have no will to go away with Siggeir, neither does my heart smile upon him; and I wot, by my fore-knowledge, and from the fetch of our kin, that from this counsel will great evil fall on us if this wedding be not speedily undone."

"Speak in no such wise, daughter!" said he; "for great shame will it be to him, yea, and to us also, to break troth with him, he being sackless; and in naught may we trust him, and no friendship shall we have of him, if these matters are broken off; but he will pay us back in as evil wise as he may; for that alone is seemly, to hold truly to troth given."

So King Siggeir got ready for home, and before he went from the feast he bade King Volsung, his father-in-law, come see him in Gothland, and all his sons with him, whenas three months should be overpast, and to bring such following with him, as he would have, and as he deemed meet for his honour; and thereby will Siggeir the king pay back for the shortcomings of the wedding-feast, in that he would abide thereat but one night only, a thing not according to the wont of men. So King Volsung gave his word to come on the day named, and the kinsmen-in-law parted, and Siggeir went home with his wife.

Chapter 5

Of the Slaying of King Volsung

Now TELLS the tale of King Volsung and his sons that they go at the time appointed to Gothland at the bidding of King Siggeir, and put off from the land in three ships, all well manned, and have a fair voyage, and made Gothland late of an evening tide.

But that same night came Signy and called her father and brothers to a privy talk, and told them what she deemed King Siggeir was minded to do, and how that he had drawn together an army no man may meet. "And," says she, "he is minded to do guilefully by you; wherefore I bid you get ye gone back again to your own land, and gather together the mightiest power ye may, and then come back hither and avenge you; neither go ye now to your undoing, for ye shall surely fail not to fall by his wiles if ye turn not on him even as I bid you."

Then spake Volsung the king, "All people and nations shall tell of the word I spake, yet being unborn, wherein I vowed a vow that I would flee in fear from neither fire nor the sword; even so have I done hitherto, and shall I depart therefrom now I am old? Yea withal never shall the maidens mock these my sons at the games, and cry out at them that they fear death; once alone must all men need die, and from that season shall none escape; so my rede it is that we flee nowhither, but do the work of our hands in as manly wise as we may; a hundred

97

fights have I fought, and whiles I had more, and whiles I had less, and yet ever had I the victory, nor shall it ever be heard tell of me that I fled away or prayed for peace."

Then Signy wept right sore, and prayed that she might not go back to King Siggeir, but King Volsung answered—

"Thou shalt surely go back to thine husband, and abide with him, howsoever it fares with us."

So Signy went home, and they abode there that night; but in the morning, as soon as it was day, Volsung bade his men arise and go aland and make them ready for battle; so they went aland, all of them all-armed, and had not long to wait before Siggeir fell on them with all his army, and the fiercest fight there was betwixt them; and Siggeir cried on his men to the onset all he might; and so the tale tells that King Volsung and his sons went eight times right through Siggeir's folk that day, smiting and hewing on either hand, but when they would do so even once again, King Volsung fell amidst his folk and all his men withal, saving his ten sons, for mightier was the power against them than they might withstand.

But now are all his sons taken, and laid in bonds and led away; and Signy was ware withal that her father was slain, and her brothers taken and doomed to death; that she called King Siggeir apart to talk with her, and said—

"This will I pray of thee, that thou let not slay my brothers hastily, but let them be set awhile in the stocks, for home to me comes the saw that says, *Sweet to eye while seen:* but longer life I pray not for them, because I wot well that my prayer will not avail me."

Then answered Siggeir—

"Surely thou art mad and witless, praying thus for more bale for thy brothers than their present slaying; yet this will I grant thee, for the better it likes me the more they must bear, and the longer their pain is or ever death come to them."

Now he let it be done even as she prayed, and a mighty beam was brought and set on the feet of those ten brethren in a certain place of the wild-wood, and there they sit day-long until night; but at midnight, as they sat in the stocks, there came on them a she-wolf from out the wood; old she was, and both great and evil of aspect; and the first thing she did was to bite one of those brethren till he died, and then she ate him up withal, and went on her way.

But the next morning Signy sent a man to the brethren, ever one whom she most trusted, to wot of the tidings; and when he came back he told her that one of them was dead, and great and grievous she deemed it, if they should all fare in like wise, and yet naught might she avail them.

Soon is the tale told thereof: nine nights together came the she-wolf at midnight, and each night slew and ate up one of the brethren, until all were dead, save Sigmund only; so now, before the tenth night came, Signy sent that trusty man to Sigmund, her brother, and gave honey into his hand, bidding him do it over Sigmund's face, and set a little deal of it in his mouth; so he went to Sigmund and did as he was bidden, and then came home again; and so the next night came the she-wolf according to her wont, and would slay him and eat him even as his brothers; but now she sniffs the breeze from him, whereas he was anointed with the honey, and licks his face all over with her tongue, and then trusts her tongue into the mouth of him. No fear he had thereof, but caught the she-wolf's tongue betwixt his teeth, and so hard she started back thereat, and pulled herself away so mightily, setting her feet against the stocks, that all was riven asunder; but he ever held so fast that the tongue came away by the roots, and thereof she had her bane.

But some men say that this same she-wolf was the mother of King Siggeir, who had turned herself into this likeness by troll's lore and witchcraft.

Chapter 6

Of how Signy sent the Children of her and Siggeir to Sigmund

Now WHENAS Sigmund is loosed and the stocks are broken, he dwells in the woods and holds himself there; but Signy sends yet again to wot of the tidings, whether Sigmund were alive or no; but when those who were sent came to him, he told them all as it had betid, and how things had gone betwixt him and the wolf; so they went home and tell Signy the tidings; but she goes and finds her brother, and they take counsel in such wise as to make a house underground in the wild-wood; and so things go on a while, Signy hiding him there, and sending him such things as he needed; but King Siggeir deemed that all the Volsungs were dead.

Now Siggeir had two sons by his wife, whereof it is told that when the eldest was ten winters old, Signy sends him to Sigmund, so that he might give him help, if he would in any wise strive to avenge his father; so the youngling goes to the wood, and comes late in evening-tide to Sigmund's earth-house; and Sigmund welcomed him in seemly fashion, and said that he should make ready their bread; "but I," said he, "will go seek firewood."

Therewith he gives the meal-bag into his hands while he himself went to fetch firing; but when he came back the youngling had done naught at the bread-making. Then asks Sigmund if the bread be ready—

Says the youngling, "I durst not set hand to the meal-sack, because somewhat quick lay in the meal."

Now Sigmund deemed he wotted that the lad was of no such heart as that he would be fain to have him for his fellow; and when he met his sister, Sigmund said that he had come no nigher to the aid of a man though the youngling were with him.

Then said Signy, "Take him and kill him then; for why should such an one live longer?" and even so he did.

So this winter wears, and the next winter Signy sent her next son to Sigmund; and there is no need to make a long tale thereof, for in like wise went all things, and he slew the child by the counsel of Signy.

Chapter 7

Of the Birth of Sinfjotli, the Son of Sigmund

So on a tide it befell as Signy sat in her bower, that there came to her a witch-wife exceeding cunning, and Signy talked with her in such wise, "Fain am I," says she, "that we should change semblances together."

She says, "Even as thou wilt then."

And so by her wiles she brought it about that they changed semblances, and now the witch-wife sits in Signy's place according to her rede, and goes to bed by the king that night, and he knows not that he has other than Signy beside him.

But the tale tells of Signy, that she fared to the earth-house of her brother, and prayed him give her harbouring for the night; "For I have gone astray abroad in the woods, and know not whither I am going."

So he said she might abide, and that he would not refuse harbour to one lone woman, deeming that she would scarce pay back his good cheer by tale-bearing: so she came into the house, and they sat down to meat, and his eyes were often on her, and a goodly and fair woman she seemed to him; but when they are full, then he says to her, that he is right fain that they should have but one bed that night; she nowise turned away therefrom, and so for three nights together he laid her in bed by him.

Thereafter she fared home, and found the witch-wife, and bade her change semblances again, and she did so.

Now as time wears, Signy brings forth a man-child, who was named Sinfjotli, and when he grew up he was both big and strong, and fair of face, and much like unto the kin of the Volsungs, and he was hardly yet ten winters old when she sent him to Sigmund's earth-house; but this trial she had made of her other sons or ever she had sent them to Sigmund, that she had sewed gloves on to their hands through flesh and skin, and they had borne it ill and cried out thereat; and this she now did to Sinfjotli, and he changed countenance in nowise thereat. Then she flayed off the kirtle so that the skin came off with the sleeves, and said that this would be torment enough for him; but he said—

"Full little would Volsung have felt such a smart as this."

So the lad came to Sigmund, and Sigmund bade him knead their meal up, while he goes to fetch firing; so he gave him the meal-sack, and then went after the wood, and by then he came back had Sinfjotli made an end of his baking. Then asked Sigmund if he had found nothing in the meal.

"I misdoubted me that there was something quick in the meal when I first fell to kneading of it, but I have kneaded it all up together, both the meal and that which was therein, whatsoever it was."

Then Sigmund laughed out, he said—

"Naught wilt thou eat of this bread to-night, for the most deadly of worms hast thou kneaded up therewith."

Now Sigmund was so mighty a man that he might eat venom and have no hurt therefrom; but Sinfjotli might abide whatso venom came on the outside of him, but might neither eat nor drink thereof.

Chapter 8

The Death of King Siggeir and of Signy

THE TALE tells that Sigmund thought Sinfjotli over young to help him to his revenge, and will first of all harden him with manly deeds; so in summer-tide they fare wide through the woods and slay men for their wealth; Sigmund deems him to take much after the kin of the Volsungs, though he thinks that he is Siggeir's son, and deems him to have the evil heart of his father, with the might and daring of the Volsungs; withal he must needs think him in nowise a kinsome man, for full oft would he bring Sigmund's wrongs to his memory, and prick him on to slay King Siggeir.

Now on a time as they fare abroad in the woods for the getting of wealth, they find a certain house, and two men with great gold rings asleep therein: now these twain were spell-bound skin-changers, and wolf-skins were hanging up over them in the house; and every tenth day might they come out of those skins; and they were kings' sons: so Sigmund and Sinfjotli do the wolf-skins on them, and then might they no-wise come out of them, though forsooth the same nature went with them as heretofore; they howled as wolves howl, but both knew the meaning of that howling; they lay out in the wild-wood, and each went his way; and a word they made betwixt them, that they should risk the onset of seven men, but no more, and that he who was first to be set on should howl in wolfish wise: "Let us not depart from this," says Sigmund, "for thou art young and over-bold, and men will deem the quarry good, when they take thee."

Now each goes his way, and when they were parted, Sigmund meets certain men, and gives forth a wolf's howl; and when Sinfjotli heard it, he went straightway thereto, and slew them all, and once more they parted. But ere Sinfjotli has fared long through the woods, eleven men meet him, and he wrought in such wise that he slew them all, and was awearied therewith, and crawls under an oak, and there takes his rest. Then came Sigmund thither, and said—

"Why didst thou not call on me?"

Sinfjotli said, "I was loth to call for thy help for the slaying of eleven men."

Then Sigmund rushed at him so hard that he staggered and fell, and Sigmund bit him in the throat. Now that day they might not come out of their wolf-skins: but Sigmund lays the other on his back, and bears him home to the house, and cursed the wolf-gears and gave them to the trolls. Now on a day he saw where two weasels went, and how that one bit the other in the throat, and then ran straightway into the thicket, and took up a leaf and laid it on the wound, and thereon his fellow sprang up quite and clean whole; so Sigmund went out and saw a raven flying with a blade of that same herb to him; so he took it and drew it over Sinfjotli's hurt, and he straightway sprang up as whole as though he had never been hurt. Thereafter they went home to their earth-house, and abode there till the time came for them to put off the wolf-shapes; then they burnt them up with fire, and prayed that no more hurt might come to any one from them; but in that uncouth guise they wrought many famous deeds in the kingdom and lordship of King Siggeir.

Now when Sinfjotli was come to man's estate, Sigmund deemed he had tried him fully, and or ever a long time has gone by he turns his mind to the avenging of his father, if so it may be brought about; so on a certain day the twain get them gone from their earth-house, and come to the abode of King Siggeir late in the evening, and go into the porch before the hall, wherein were tuns of ale, and there they lie hid: now the queen is ware of them, where they are, and is fain to meet them; and when they met they took counsel, and were of one mind that Volsung should be revenged that same night.

Now Signy and the king had two children of tender age, who played with a golden toy on the floor, and bowled it along the pavement of the hall, running along with it; but therewith a golden ring from off it trundles away into the place where Sigmund and Sinfjotli lay, and off runs the little one to search for the same, and beholds withal where two men are sitting, big and grimly to look on, with overhanging helms and bright white byrnies; so he runs up the hall to his father, and tells him of the sight he has seen, and thereat the king misdoubts of some guile abiding him; but Signy heard their speech, and arose and took both the children, and went out into the porch to them and said—

"Lo ye! these younglings have bewrayed you; come now therefore and slay them!"

Sigmund says, "Never will I slay thy children for telling of where I lay hid."

But Sinfjotli made little enow of it, but drew his sword and slew them both, and cast them into the hall at King Siggeir's feet.

Then up stood the king and cried on his men to take those who had lain privily in the porch through the night. So they ran thither and would lay hands on them, but they stood on their defence well and manly, and long he remembered it who was the nighest to them; but in the end they were borne down by many men and taken, and bonds were set upon them, and they were cast into fetters wherein they sit night long.

Then the king ponders what longest and worst of deaths he shall mete out to them; and when morning came he let make a great barrow of stones and turf; and when it was done, let set a great flat stone midmost inside thereof, so that one edge was aloft, the other alow; and so great it was that it went from wall to wall, so that none might pass it.

Now he bids folk take Sigmund and Sinfjotli and set them in the barrow, on either side of the stone, for the worse for them he deemed it, that they might hear each the other's speech, and yet that neither might pass one to the other. But now, while they were covering in the barrow with the turf-slips, thither came Signy, bearing straw with her, and cast it down to Sinfjotli, and bade the thralls hide this thing from the king; they said yea thereto, and therewithal was the barrow closed in.

But when night fell, Sinfjotli said to Sigmund, "Belike we shall scarce need meat for a while, for here has the queen cast swine's flesh into the barrow, and wrapped it round about on the outer side with straw."

Therewith he handles the flesh and finds that therein was thrust Sigmund's sword; and he knew it by the hilts, as mirk as it might be in the barrow, and tells Sigmund thereof, and of that were they both fain enow.

Now Sinfjotli drave the point of the sword up into the big stone, and drew it hard along, and the sword bit on the stone. With that Sigmund caught the sword by the point, and in this wise they sawed the stone between them, and let not or all the sawing was done that need be done, even as the song sings:

"Sinfjotli sawed
And Sigmund sawed,
Atwain with main
The stone was done."

Now are they both together loose in the barrow, and soon they cut both through stone and through iron, and bring themselves out thereof. Then they go home to the hall, whenas all men slept there, and bear wood to the hall, and lay fire therein; and withal the folk therein are waked by the smoke, and by the hall burning over their heads.

Then the king cries out, "Who kindled this fire, I burn withal?"

"Here am I," says Sigmund, "with Sinfjotli, my sister's son; and we are minded that thou shalt wot well that all the Volsungs are not yet dead."

Then he bade his sister come out, and take all good things at his hands, and great honour, and fair atonement in that wise, for all her griefs.

But she answered, "Take heed now, and consider, if I have kept King Siggeir in memory, and his slaying of Volsung the king! I let slay both my children, whom I deemed worthless for the revenging of our father, and I went into the wood to thee in a witch-wife's shape; and now behold, Sinfjotli is the son of thee and of me both! and therefore has he this so great hardihood and fierceness, in that he is the son both of Volsung's son and Volsung's daughter; and for this, and for naught else, have I so wrought, that Siggeir might get his bane at last; and all these things have I done that vengeance might fall on him, and that I too might not live long; and merrily now will I die with King Siggeir, though I was naught merry to wed him."

Therewith she kissed Sigmund her brother, and Sinfjotli, and went back again into the fire, and there she died with King Siggeir and all his good men.

But the two kinsmen gathered together folk and ships, and Sigmund went back to his father's land, and drave away thence the king, who had set himself down there in the room of king Volsung.

So Sigmund became a mighty King and far-famed, wise and high-minded: he had to wife one named Borghild, and two sons they had between them, one named Helgi and the other Hamund; and when Helgi was born, Norns came to him, and spake over him, and said that he should be in time to come the most renowned of all kings. Even therewith was Sigmund come home from the wars, and so therewith he gives him the name of Helgi, and these matters as tokens thereof, Land of Rings, Sun-litten Hill, and Sharp-shearing Sword, and withal prayed that he might grow of great fame, and like unto the kin of the Volsungs.

And so it was he grew up high-minded, and well-beloved, and above all other men in all prowess; and the story tells that he went to the wars when he was fifteen winters old. Helgi was lord and ruler over the army, but Sinfjotli was gotten to be his fellow herein; and so the twain bare sway thereover.

Chapter 9

How Helgi, the son of Sigmund, won King Hodbrod and his Realm, and Wedded Sigrun

Now THE tale tells that Helgi in his warring met a king hight Hunding, a mighty king, and lord of many men and many lands; they fell to battle together, and Helgi went forth mightily, and such was the end of that fight that Helgi had the victory, but King Hunding fell and many of his men with him; but Helgi is deemed to have grown greatly in fame because he had slain so mighty a king.

Then the sons of Hunding draw together a great army to avenge their father. Hard was the fight betwixt them; but Helgi goes through the folk of those brothers unto their banner, and there slays these sons of Hunding, Alf and Eyolf, Herward and Hagbard, and wins there a great victory.

Now as Helgi fared from the fight, he met a many women right fair and worthy to look on, who rode in exceeding noble array; but one far excelled them all; then Helgi asked them the name of that their lady and queen, and she named herself Sigrun, and said she was daughter of King Hogni.

Then said Helgi, "Fare home with us: good welcome shall ye have!"

Then said the king's daughter, "Other work lies before us than to drink with thee."

"Yea, and what work, king's daughter?" said Helgi.

She answers, "King Hogni has promised me to Hodbrod, the son of King Granmar, but I have vowed a vow that I will have him to my husband no more than if he were a crow's son and not a king's; and yet will the thing come to pass, but and if thou standest in the way thereof, and goest against him with an army, and takest me away withal; for verily with no king would I rather bide on bolster than with thee."

"Be of good cheer, king's daughter," says he, "for certes he and I shall try the matter, or ever thou be given to him; yea, we shall behold which may prevail against the other; and hereto I pledge my life."

Threafter, Helgi sent men with money in their hands to summon his folk to him, and all his power is called together to Red-Berg: and there Helgi abode till such time as a great company came to him from Hedinsey; and therewithal came mighty power from Norvi Sound aboard great and fair ships. Then King Helgi called to him the captain of his ships, who was hight Leif, and asked him if he had told over the tale of his army.

"A thing not easy to tell, lord," says he, "on the ships that came out of Norvi Sound are twelve thousand men, and otherwhere are half as many again."

Then bade King Helgi turn into the firth, called Varin's-firth, and they did so: but now there fell on them so fierce a storm and so huge a sea, that the beat of the waves on board and bow was to hearken to like as the clashing together of high hills broken.

But Helgi bade men fear naught, nor take in any sail, but rather hoist every rag higher than heretofore; but little did they miss of foundering or ever they made land; then came Sigrun, daughter of King Hogni, down on to the beach with a great army, and turned them away thence to a good haven called Gnipalund; but the landsmen see what has befallen and come down to the sea-shore. The brother of King Hodbrod, lord of a land called Swarin's Cairn, cried out to them, and asked them who was captain over that mighty army. Then up stands Sinfjotli, with a helm on his head, bright shining as glass, and a byrny as white as snow; a spear in his hand, and thereon a banner of renown, and a gold-rimmed shield hang-

ing before him; and well he knew with what words to speak
to kings—

"Go thou and say, when thou hast made an end of feeding
thy swine and thy dogs, and when thou beholdest thy wife
again, that here are come the Volsungs, and in this company
may King Helgi be found, if Hodbrod be fain of finding him,
for his game and his joy it is to fight and win fame, while thou
art kissing the handmaids by the fireside."

Then answered Granmar, "In nowise knowest thou how to
speak seemly things, and to tell of matters remembered from
of old, whereas thou layest lies on chiefs and lords; most like
it is that thou must have long been nourished with wolf-meat
abroad in the wild-woods, and has slain thy brethren; and a
marvel it is to behold that thou darest to join thyself to the
company of good men and true, thou, who hast sucked the
blood of many a cold corpse."

Sinfjotli answered, "Dim belike is grown thy memory now,
of how thou wert a witch-wife on Varinsey, and wouldst fain
have a man to thee, and chose me to that same office of all
the world; and how thereafter thou wert a Valkyria in Asgarth,
and it well-nigh came to this, that for thy sweet sake should all
men fight; and nine wolf-whelps I begat on thy body in Low-
ness, and was the father to them all."

Granmar answers, "Great skill of lying hast thou; yet belike
the father of naught at all mayst thou be, since thou wert
gelded by the giant's daughters of Thrasness; and lo thou art
the stepson of King Siggeir, and were wont to lie abroad in
wilds and woods with the kin of wolves; and unlucky was the
hand wherewith thou slewest thy brethren, making for thyself
an exceeding evil name."

Said Sinfjotli, "Mindest thou not then, when thou were
stallion Grani's mare, and how I rode thee an amble on
Bravoll, and that afterwards thou wert giant Golnir's goat-
herd?"

Granmar says, "Rather would I feed fowls with the flesh of
thee than wrangle any longer with thee."

Then spake King Helgi, "Better were it for ye, and a more
manly deed, to fight, rather than to speak such things as it is

a shame even to hearken to; Granmar's sons are no friends of me and of mine, yet are they hardy men none the less."

So Granmar rode away to meet King Hodbrod, at a stead called Sunfells, and the horses of the twain were named Sveipud and Sveggjud. The brothers met in the castle-porch, and Granmar told Hodbrod of the war-news, King Hodbrod was clad in a byrny, and had his helm on his head; he asked—

"What men are anigh, why look ye so wrathful?"

Granmar says, "Here are come the Volsungs, and twelve thousand men of them are afloat off the coast, and seven thousand are at the island called Sok, but at the stead called Grindur is the greatest company of all, and now I deem withal that Helgi and his fellowship have good will to give battle."

Then said the king, "Let us send a message through all our realm, and go against them, neither let any who is fain of fight sit idle at home; let us send word to the sons of Ring, and to King Hogni, and to Alf the Old, for they are mighty warriors."

So the hosts met at Wolfstone, and fierce fight befell there; Helgi rushed forth through the host of his foes, and many a man fell there; at last folk saw a great company of shield-maidens, like burning flames to look on, and there was come Sigrun, the king's daughter. Then King Helgi fell on King Hodbrod, and smote him, and slew him even under his very banner; and Sigrun cried out—

"Have thou thanks for thy so manly deed! now shall we share the land between us, and a day of great good hap this is to me, and for this deed shalt thou get honour and renown, in that thou hast felled to earth so mighty a king."

So Helgi took to him that realm and dwelt there long, when he had wedded Sigrun, and became a king of great honour and renown, though he has naught more to do with this story.

Chapter 10

The Ending of Sinfjotli, Sigmund's Son

Now THE Volsungs fare back home, and have gained great renown by these deeds. But Sinfjotli betook himself to warfare anew; and therewith he had sight of an exceeding fair woman, and yearned above all things for her; but that same woman was wooed also of the brother of Borghild, the king's wife: and this matter they fought out betwixt them, and Sinfjotli slew that king; and thereafter he harried far and wide, and had many a battle and ever gained the day; and he became hereby honoured and renowned above all men; but in autumn tide he came home with many ships and abundant wealth.

Then he told his tidings to the king his father, and he again to the queen, and she for her part bids him get him gone from the realm, and made as if she would in nowise see him. But Sigmund said he would not drive him away, and offered her atonement of gold and great wealth for her brother's life, albeit he said he had never erst given weregild to any for the slaying of a man, but no fame it was to uphold wrong against a woman.

So seeing she might not get her own way herein, she said, "Have thy will in this matter, O my lord, for it is seemly so to be."

And now she holds the funeral feast for her brother by the aid and counsel of the king, and makes ready all things therefor in the best of wise, and bade thither many great men.

At that feast, Borghild the queen bare the drink to folk, and she came over against Sinfjotli with a great horn, and said—

"Fall to now and drink, fair stepson!"

Then he took the horn to him, and looked therein, and said—

"Nay, for the drink is charmed drink."

Then said Sigmund, "Give it unto me then;" and therewith he took the horn and drank it off.

But the queen said to Sinfjotli, "Why must other men needs drink thine ale for thee?" And she came again the second time with the horn, and said, "Come now and drink!" and goaded him with many words.

And he took the horn, and said—

"Guile is in the drink."

And thereon, Sigmund cried out—

"Give it then unto me!"

Again, the third time, she came to him, and bade him drink off his drink, if he had the heart of a Volsung; then he laid hand on the horn, but said—

"Venom is therein."

"Nay, let the lip strain it out then, O son," quoth Sigmund; and by then was he exceeding drunk with drink, and therefore spake he in that wise.

So Sinfjotli drank, and straightway fell down dead to the ground.

Sigmund rose up, and sorrowed nigh to death over him; then he took the corpse in his arms and fared away to the wood, and went till he came to a certain firth; and there he saw a man in a little boat; and that man asked if he would be wafted by him over the firth, and he said yea thereto; but so little was the boat, that they might not all go in it at once, so the corpse was first laid therein, while Sigmund went by the firth-side. But therewith the boat and the man therein vanished away from before Sigmund's eyes.

So thereafter Sigmund turned back home, and drave away the queen, and a little after she died. But Sigmund the king yet ruled his realm, and is deemed ever the greatest champion and king of the old law.

Chapter 11

Of King Sigmund's last Battle, and of how he must yield up his Sword again

THERE WAS a king called Eylimi, mighty and of great fame, and his daughter was called Hjordis, the fairest and wisest of womankind; and Sigmund hears it told of her that she was meet to be his wife, yea if none else were. So he goes to the house of King Eylimi, who would make a great feast for him, if so be he comes not thither in the guise of a foe. So messages were sent from one to the other that this present journey was a peaceful one, and not for war; so the feast was held in the best of wise and with many a man thereat; fairs were in every place established for King Sigmund, and all things else were done to the aid and comfort of his journey: so he came to the feast, and both kings hold their state in one hall; thither also was come King Lyngi, son of King Hunding, and he also is a-wooing the daughter of King Eylimi.

Now the king deemed he knew that the twain had come thither but for one errand, and thought withal that war and trouble might be looked for from the hands of him who brought not his end about; so he spake to his daughter, and said—

"Thou art a wise woman, and I have spoken it, that thou alone shalt choose a husband for thyself; choose therefore between these two kings, and my rede shall be even as thine."

"A hard and troublous matter," says she; "yet will I choose

117

him who is of greatest fame, King Sigmund to wit, albeit he is well stricken in years."

So to him was she betrothed, and King Lyngi gat him gone. Then was Sigmund wedded to Hjordis, and now each day was the feast better and more glorious than on the day before it. But thereafter Sigmund went back home to Hunland, and King Eylimi, his father-in-law, with him, and King Sigmund betakes himself to the due ruling of his realm.

But King Lyngi and his brethren gather an army together to fall on Sigmund, for as in all matters they were wont to have the worser lot, so did this bite the sorest of all; and they would fain prevail over the might and pride of the Volsungs. So they came to Hunland, and sent King Sigmund word how that they would not steal upon him, and that they deemed he would scarce slink away from them. So Sigmund said he would come and meet them in battle, and drew his power together; but Hjordis was borne into the wood with a certain bondmaid, and mighty wealth went with them; and there she abode the while they fought.

Now the vikings rushed from their ships in numbers not to be borne up against, but Sigmund the King, and Eylimi, set up their banners, and the horns blew up to battle; but King Sigmund let blow the horn his father erst had had, and cheered on his men to the fight, but his army was far the fewest.

Now was that battle fierce and fell, and though Sigmund were old, yet most hardily he fought, and was ever the foremost of his men; no shield or byrny might hold against him, and he went ever through the ranks of his foemen on that day, and no man might see how things would fare between them; many an arrow and many a spear was aloft in air that day, and so his spae-wrights wrought for him that he got no wound, and none can tell over the tale of those who fell before him, and both his arms were red with blood, even to the shoulders.

But now whenas the battle had dured a while, there came a man into the fight clad in a blue cloak, and with a slouched hat on his head, one-eyed he was, and bare a bill in his hand; and he came against Sigmund the King, and have up his bill against him, and as Sigmund smote fiercely with the sword it fell upon the bill and burst asunder in the midst: thenceforth the slaughter and dismay turned to his side, for the good-hap of King Sigmund had departed from him, and his men fell fast about him; naught did the king spare himself, but he rather cheered on his men; but even as the saw says, *No might 'gainst many*, so was it now proven; and in this fight fell Sigmund the King, and King Eylimi, his father-in-law, in the fore-front of their battle, and therewith the more part of their folk.

Chapter 12

Of the Shards of the Sword Gram, and how Hjordis went to King Alf

Now KING LYNGI made for the king's abode, and was minded to take the king's daughter there, but failed herein, for there he found neither wife nor wealth: so he fared through all the realm, and gave his men rule thereover, and now deemed that he had slain all the kin of the Volsungs, and that he need dread them no more from henceforth.

Now Hjordis went amidst the slain that night of the battle, and came whereas lay King Sigmund, and asked if he might be healed; but he answered—

"Many a man lives after hope has grown little; but my good-hap has departed from me, nor will I suffer myself to be healed, nor wills Odin that I should ever draw sword again, since this my sword and his is broken; lo now, I have waged war while it was his will."

"Naught ill would I deem matters," said she, "if thou mightest be healed and avenge my father."

The king said, "That is fated for another man; behold now, thou are great with a man-child; nourish him well and with good heed, and the child shall be the noblest and most famed of all our kin: and keep well withal the shards of the sword: thereof shall a goodly sword be made, and it shall be called Gram, and our son shall bear it, and shall work many a great work therewith, even such as eld shall never minish; for his

121

name shall abide and flourish as long as the world shall endure: and let this be enow for thee. But now I grow weary
with my wounds, and I will go see our kin that have gone
before me."

So Hjordis sat over him till he died at the day-dawning; and
then she looked, and behold, there came many ships sailing to
the land: then she spake to the handmaid—

"Let us now change raiment, and be thou called by my
name, and say that thou art the king's daughter."

And thus they did; but now the vikings behold the great
slaughter of men there, and see where two women fare away
thence into the wood; and they deem that some great tidings
must have befallen, and they leaped ashore from out their
ships. Now the captain of these folks was Alf, son of Hjalprek,
king of Denmark, who was sailing with his power along the
land. So they came into the field among the slain, and saw
how many men lay dead there; then the king bade go seek for
the women and bring them thither, and they did so. He asked
them what women they were; and, little as the thing seems
like to be, the bondmaid answered for the twain, telling of the
fall of King Sigmund and King Eylimi, and many another
great man, and who they were withal who had wrought the
deed. Then the king asks if they wotted where the wealth of
the king was bestowed; and then says the bondmaid—

"It may well be deemed that we know full surely thereof."

And therewith she guides them to the place where the
treasure lay: and there they found exceeding great wealth; so
that men deem they have never seen so many things of price
heaped up together in one place. All this they bore to the ships
of King Alf, and Hjordis and the bondmaid went with them.
Therewith these sail away to their own realm, and talk how
that surely on that field had fallen the most renowned of kings.

So the king sits by the tiller, but the women abide in the
forecastle; but talk he had with the women and held their
counsels of much account.

In such wise the king came home to his realm with great
wealth, and he himself was a man exceeding goodly to look
on. But when he had been but a little while at home, the
queen, his mother, asked him why the fairest of the two
women had the fewer rings and the less worthy attire.

"I deem," she said, "that she whom ye have held of least account is the noblest of the twain."

He answered: "I too have misdoubted me, that she is little like a bondwoman, and when we first met, in seemly wise she greeted noble men. Lo now, we will make a trial of the thing."

So on a time as men sat at the drink, the king sat down to talk with the women, and said—

"In what wise do ye note the wearing of the hours, whenas night grows old, if ye may not see the lights of heaven?"

Then says the bondwoman, "This sign have I, that whenas in my youth I was wont to drink much in the dawn, so now when I no longer use that manner, I am yet wont to wake up at the very same tide, and by that token do I know thereof."

Then the king laughed and said, "Ill manners for king's daughter!" And therewith he turned to Hjordis, and asked her even the same question; but she answered—

"My father erst gave me a little gold ring of such nature, that it groweth cold on my finger in the day-dawning; and that is the sign that I have to know thereof."

The king answered: "Enow of gold there, where a very bondmaid bore it! but come now, thou hast been long enow hid from me; yet if thou hadst told me all from the beginning, I would have done to thee as though we had both been one king's children: but better than thy deeds will I deal with thee, for thou shalt be my wife, and due jointure will I pay thee whenas thou hast borne me a child."

She spake therewith and told out the whole truth about herself: so there was she held in great honour, and deemed the worthiest of women.

Chapter 13

Of the Birth and Waxing of Sigurd Fafnir's-bane

THE TALE tells that Hjordis brought forth a man-child, who was straightly borne before King Hjalprek, and then was the king glad thereof, when he saw the keen eyes in the head of him, and he said that few men would be equal to him or like unto him in any wise. So he was sprinkled with water, and had to name Sigurd, of whom all men speak with one speech and say that none was ever his like for growth and goodliness. He was brought up in the house of King Hjalprek in great love and honour; and so it is, that whenso all the noblest men and greatest kings are named in the olden tales, Sigurd is ever put before them all, for might and prowess, for high mind and stout heart, wherewith he was far more abundantly gifted than any man of the northern parts of the wide world.

So Sigurd waxed in King Hjalprek's house, and there was no child but loved him; through him was Hjordis bethrothed to King Alf, and jointure meted to her.

Now Sigurd's foster-father was hight Regin, the son of Hreidmar; he taught him all manner of arts, the chess play, and the lore of runes, and the talking of many tongues, even as the wont was with kings' sons in those days. But on a day when they were together, Regin asked Sigurd, if he knew how much wealth his father had owned, and who had the ward thereof; Sigurd answered, and said that the kings kept the ward thereof.

Said Regin, "Dost thou trust them all utterly?"

Sigurd said, "It is seemly that they keep it till I may do somewhat therewith, for better they wot how to guard it than I do."

Another time came Regin to talk to Sigurd, and said—

"A marvellous thing truly that thou must needs be a horse-boy to the kings, and go about like a running knave."

"Nay," said Sigurd, "it is not so, for in all things I have my will, and whatso thing I desire is granted me with good will."

"Well, then," said Regin, "ask for a horse of them."

"Yea," quoth Sigurd, "and that shall I have, whenso I have need thereof."

Thereafter Sigurd went to the king, and the king said—

"What wilt thou have of us?"

Then said Sigurd, "I would even a horse of thee for my disport."

Then said the king, "Choose for thyself a horse, and whatso thing else thou desirest among my matters."

So the next day went Sigurd to the wood, and met on the way an old man, long-bearded, that he knew not, who asked him whither away.

Sigurd said, "I am minded to choose me a horse; come thou, and counsel me thereon."

"Well then," said he, "go we and drive them to the river which is called Busil-tarn."

They did so, and drave the horses down into the deeps of the river, and all swam back to land but one horse; and that horse Sigurd chose for himself; grey he was of hue, and young of years, great of growth, and fair to look on, nor had any man yet crossed his back.

Then spake the grey-beard, "From Sleipnir's kin is this horse come, and he must be nourished heedfully, for it will be the best of all horses;" and therewithal he vanished away.

So Sigurd called the horse Grani, the best of all the horses of the world; nor was the man he met other than Odin himself.

Now yet again spake Regin to Sigurd, and said—

"Not enough is thy wealth, and I grieve right sore that thou must needs run here and there like a churl's son; but I can tell thee where there is much wealth for the winning, and great name and honour to be won in the getting of it."

Sigurd asked where that might be, and who had watch and ward over it.

Regin answered, "Fafnir is his name, and but a little way hence he lies, on the waste of Gnita-heath; and when thou comest there thou mayst well say that thou hast never seen more gold heaped together in one place, and that none might desire more treasure, though he were the most ancient and famed of all kings."

"Young am I," says Sigurd, "yet know I the fashion of this worm, and how that none durst go against him, so huge and evil is he."

Regin said, "Nay it is not so, the fashion and the growth of him is even as of other lingworms, and an over great tale men make of it; and even so would thy forefathers have deemed; but thou, though thou be of the kin of the Volsungs, shalt scarce have the heart and mind of those, who are told of as the first in all deeds of fame."

Sigurd said, "Yea, belike I have little of their hardihood and prowess, but thou has naught to do, to lay a coward's name upon me, when I am scarce out of my childish years. Why dost thou egg me on hereto so busily?"

Regin said, "Therein lies a tale which I must needs tell thee."

"Let me hear the same," said Sigurd.

Chapter 14

Regin's tale of his Brothers, and of the Gold called Andvari's Hoard

"THUS THE tale begins," said Regin. "Hreidmar was my father's name, a mighty man and a wealthy: and his first son was named Fafnir, his second Otter, and I was the third, and the least of them all both for prowess and good conditions, but I was cunning to work in iron, and silver, and gold, whereof I could make matters that availed somewhat. Other skill my brother Otter followed, and had another nature withal, for he was a great fisher, and above other men herein; in that he had the likeness of an otter by day, and dwelt ever in the river, and bare fish to bank in his mouth, and his prey would he ever bring to our father, and that availed him much: for the most part he kept him in his otter-gear, and then he would come home, and eat alone, and slumbering, for on the dry land he might see naught. But Fafnir was by far the greatest and grimmest, and would have all things about called his.

"Now," says Regin, "there was a dwarf called Andvari, who ever abode in that force, which was called Andvari's force, in the likeness of a pike, and got meat for himself, for many fish there were in the force; now Otter, my brother, was ever wont to enter into the force, and bring fish aland, and lay them one by one on the bank. And so it befell that Odin, Loki, and Hœnir, as they went their ways, came to Andvari's force, and Otter had taken a salmon, and ate it slumbering upon the river bank; then Loki took a stone and cast it at Otter, so that he gat his death thereby; the gods were well content with their prey, and fell to flaying off the otter's skin; and in the evening they came to Hreidmar's house, and showed him what they had taken: thereon he laid hands on them, and doomed them to such ransom, as that they should fill the otter skin with gold, and cover it over without with red gold; so they sent Loki to gather gold together for them; he came to Ran, and got her net, and went therewith to Andvari's force, and cast the net before the pike, and the pike ran into the net and was taken. Then said Loki—

> " 'What fish of all fishes,
>   Swims strong in the flood,
> But hath learnt little wit to beware?
>   Thine head must thou buy,
>   From abiding in hell,
> And find me the wan waters flame.'

He answered—

> " 'Andvari folk call me,
>   Call Oinn my father,
> Over many a force have I fared;
>   For a Norn of ill-luck,
>   This life on me lay
> Through wet ways ever to wade.'

"So Loki beheld the gold of Andvari, and when he had given up the gold, he had but one ring left, and that also Loki took from him; then the dwarf went into a hollow of the rocks, and cried out, that the gold-ring, yea and all the gold withal, should be the bane of every man who should own it thereafter.

"Now the gods rode with the treasure to Hreidmar, and fulfilled the otter-skin, and set it on its feet, and they must cover it over utterly with gold: but when this was done then Hreidmar came forth, and beheld yet one of the muzzle hairs, and bade them cover that withal; then Odin drew the ring, Andvari's loom, from his hand, and covered up the hair therewith; then sang Loki—

" 'Gold enow, gold enow,
   A great weregild, thou hast,
That my head in good hap I may hold;
   But thou and thy son
   Are naught fated to thrive,
The bane shall it be of you both.'

"Thereafter," says Regin, "Fafnir slew his father and murdered him, nor got I aught of the treasure, and so evil he grew, that he fell to lying abroad, and begrudged any share in the wealth to any man, and so became the worst of all worms, and ever now lies brooding upon that treasure: but for me, I went to the king and became his master-smith; and thus is the tale told of how I lost the heritage of my father, and the weregild for my brother."

So spake Regin; but since that time gold is called Ottergild, and for no other cause than this.

But Sigurd answered, "Much hast thou lost, and exceeding evil have thy kinsmen been! but now, make a sword by thy craft, such a sword as that none can be made like unto it; so that I may do great deeds therewith, if my heart avail thereto, and thou wouldst have me slay this mighty dragon."

Regin says, "Trust me well herein; and with that same sword shalt thou slay Fafnir."

Chapter 15

Of the Welding together of the Shards of the Sword Gram

So REGIN makes a sword, and gives it into Sigurd's hands. He took the sword, and said—

"Behold thy smithying, Regin!" and therewith smote it into the anvil, and the sword brake; so he cast down the brand, and bade him forge a better.

Then Regin forged another sword, and brought it to Sigurd, who looked thereon.

Then said Regin, "Belike thou art well content therewith, hard master though thou be in smithying."

So Sigurd proved the sword, and brake it even as the first; then he said to Regin—

"Ah, art thou, mayhappen, a traitor and a liar like to those former kin of thine?"

Therewith he went to his mother, and she welcomed him in seemly wise, and they talked and drank together.

Then spake Sigurd, "Have I heard aright, that King Sigmund gave thee the good sword Gram in two pieces?"

"True enough," she said.

So Sigurd said, "Deliver them into my hands, for I would have them."

She said he looked like to win great fame, and gave him the sword. Therewith went Sigurd to Regin, and bade him make a good sword thereof as he best might; Regin grew wroth thereat, but went into the smithy with the pieces of the sword, thinking well meanwhile that Sigurd pushed his head far enow into the matter of smithying. So he made a sword, and as he bore it forth from the forge, it seemed to the smiths as though fire burned along the edges thereof. Now he bade Sigurd take the sword, and said he knew not how to make a sword if this one failed. Then Sigurd smote it into the anvil, and cleft it down to the stock thereof, and neither burst the sword nor brake it. Then he praised the sword much, and thereafter went to the river with a lock of wool, and threw it up against the stream, and it fell asunder when it met the sword. Then was Sigurd glad, and went home.

But Regin said, "Now whereas I have made the sword for thee, belike thou wilt hold to thy troth given, and wilt go meet Fafnir?"

"Surely will I hold thereto," said Sigurd, "yet first must I avenge my father."

Now Sigurd the older he grew, the more he grew in the love of all men, so that every child loved him well.

Chapter 16

The Prophecy of Grifir

THERE WAS a man hight Grifir, who was Sigurd's mother's brother, and a little after the forging of the sword Sigurd went to Grifir, because he was a man who knew things to come, and what was fated to men: of him Sigurd asked diligently how his life should go; but Grifir was long or he spake, yet at the last, by reason of Sigurd's exceeding great prayers, he told him all his life and the fate thereof, even as afterwards came to pass. So when Grifir had told him all even as he would, he went back home; and a little after he and Regin met.

Then said Regin, "Go thou and slay Fafnir, even as thou hast given thy word."

Sigurd said, "That work shall be wrought; but another is first to be done, the avenging of Sigmund the king and the other of my kinsmen who fell in that their last fight."

Chapter 17

Of Sigurd's Avenging of Sigmund his Father

Now SIGURD went to the kings, and spake thus—

"Here have I abode a space with you, and I owe you thanks and reward, for great love and many gifts and all due honour; but now will I away from the land and go meet the sons of Hunding, and do them to wit that the Volsungs are not all dead; and your might would I have to strengthen me therein."

So the kings said that they would give him all things soever that he desired, and therewith was a great army got ready, and all things wrought in the most heedful wise, ships and all wargear, so that his journey might be of the stateliest: but Sigurd himself steered the dragon-keel which was the greatest and noblest; richly wrought were their sails, and glorious to look on.

So they said and have wind at will; but when a few days were overpast, there arose a great storm on the sea, and the waves were to behold even as the foam of men's blood; but Sigurd bade take in no sail, howsoever they might be riven, but rather to lay on higher than heretofore. But as they sailed past the rocks of a ness, a certain man hailed the ships, and asked who was captain over that navy; then was it told him that the chief and lord was Sigurd, the son of Sigmund, the most famed of all the young men who now are.

Then said the man, "Naught but one thing, certes, do all

say of him, that none among the sons of kings may be likened unto him; now fain were I that ye would shorten sail on some of the ships, and take me aboard."

Then they asked him of his name, and he sang—

> Hnikar I hight,
> When I gladdened Huginn,
> And went to battle,
> Bright son of Volsung;
> Now may ye call
> The carl on the cliff top,
> Feng or Fjolnir:
> Fain would I with you.

They made for land therewith, and took that man aboard Then quoth Sigurd, as the song says—

> Tell me this, O Hnikar,
> Since full well thou knowest
> Fate of Gods, good and ill of mankind,
> What best our hap foresheweth,
> When amid the battle
> About us sweeps the sword edge.

Quoth Hnikar—

> Good are many tokens
> If thereof men wotted
> When the swords are sweeping:
> Fair fellow deem I
> The dark-winged raven,
> In war, to weapon-wielder.

> The second good thing:
> When abroad thou goest
> For the long road well arrayed,
> Good if thou seest
> Two men standing,
> Fain of fame within the forecourt.

A third thing:
Good hearing,
The wolf a howling
Abroad under ash boughs;
Good hap shalt thou have
Dealing with helm-staves,
If thou seest these fare before thee.

No man in fight
His face shall turn
Against the moon's sister
Low, late-shining,
For he winneth battle
Who best beholdeth
Through the midmost sword-play,
And the sloping ranks best shapeth.

Great is the trouble
Of foot ill-tripping,
When arrayed for fight thou farest,
For on both sides about
Are the Dísir by thee,
Guileful, wishful of thy wounding.

Fair-combed, well washen
Let each warrior be,
Nor lack meat in the morning,
For who can rule
The eve's returning,
And base to fall before fate grovelling.

Then the storm abated, and on they fared till they came aland in the realm of Hunding's sons, and then Fjolnir vanished away.

Then they let loose fire and sword, and slew men and burnt their abodes, and did waste all before them: a great company of folk fled before the face of them to Lyngi the King, and tell him that men of war are in the land, and are faring with such rage and fury that the like has never been heard of; and that the sons of King Hunding had no great forecast in that they said they would never fear the Volsungs more, for here was come Sigurd, the son of Sigmund, as captain over this army.

So King Lyngi let send the war-message all throughout his realm, and has no will to flee, but summons to him all such as would give him aid. So he came against Sigurd with a great army, he and his brothers with him, and an exceeding fierce fight befell; many a spear and many an arrow might men see there raised aloft, axes hard driven, shields cleft and byrnies torn, helmets were shivered, skulls split atwain, and many a man felled to the cold earth.

And now when the fight has long dured in such wise, Sigurd goes forth before the banners, and has the good sword Gram in his hand, and smites down both men and horses, and goes through the thickest of the throng with both arms red with blood to the shoulder; and folk shrank aback before him wheresoever he went, nor would either helm or byrny hold before him, and no man deemed he had ever seen his like. So a long while the battle lasted, and many a man was slain, and furious was the onset; till at last it befell, even as seldom comes to hand, when a land army falls on, that, do whatso they might, naught was brought about; but so many men fell of the sons of Hunding that the tale of them may not be told; and now whenas Sigurd was among the foremost, came the sons of Hunding against him, and Sigurd smote therewith at Lyngi the king, and clave him down, both helm and head, and mail-clad body, and thereafter he smote Hjorward his brother atwain, and then slew all the other sons of Hunding who were yet alive, and the more part of their folk withal.

Now home goes Sigurd with fair victory won, and plenteous wealth and great honour, which he had gotten to him in this journey, and feasts were made for him against he came back to the realm.

But when Sigurd had been at home but a little, came Regin to talk with him, and said—

"Belike thou wilt now have good will to bow down Fafnir's crest according to thy word plighted, since thou hast thus revenged thy father and the others of thy kin."

Sigurd answered, "That will we hold to, even as we have promised, nor did it ever fall from our memory."

Chapter 18

Of the Slaying of the Worm Fafnir

Now Sigurd and Regin ride up the heath along that same way wherein Fafnir was wont to creep when he fared to the water; and folk say that thirty fathoms was the height of that cliff along which he lay when he drank of the water below. Then Sigurd spake:

"How sayedst thou, Regin, that this drake was no greater than other lingworms; methinks the track of him is marvellous great?"

Then said Regin, "Make thee a hole, and sit down therein, and whenas the worm comes to the water, smite him into the heart, and so do him to death, and win for thee great fame thereby."

But Sigurd said, "What will betide me if I be before the blood of the worm?"

Says Regin, "Of what avail to counsel thee if thou art still afeard of everything? Little art thou like thy kin in stoutness of heart."

Then Sigurd rides right over the heath; but Regin gets him gone, sore afeard.

But Sigurd fell to digging him a pit, and whiles he was at that work, there came to him an old man with a long beard, and asked what he wrought there, and he told him.

Then answered the old man and said, "Thou doest after sorry counsel: rather dig thee many pits, and let the blood run

141

therein; but sit thee down in one thereof, and so thrust the worm's heart through."

And therewithal he vanished away; but Sigurd made the pits even as it was shown to him.

Now crept the worm down to his place of watering, and the earth shook all about him, and he snorted forth venom on all the way before him as he went; but Sigurd neither trembled nor was adrad at the roaring of him. So whenas the worm crept over the pits, Sigurd thrust his sword under his left shoulder, so that it sank in up to the hilts; then up leapt Sigurd from the pit and drew the sword back again unto him, and therewith with his arm all bloody, up to the very shoulder.

Now when that mighty worm was ware that he had his death-wound, then he lashed out head and tail, so that all things soever that were before him were broken to pieces.

So whenas Fafnir had his death-wound, he asked "Who art thou? and who is thy father? and what thy kin, that thou wert so hardy as to bear weapons against me?"

Sigurd answered, "Unknown to men is my kin. I am called a noble beast: neither father have I nor mother, and all alone have I fared hither."

Said Fafnir, "Whereas thou hast neither father nor mother, of what wonder wert thou born then? But now, though thou tellest me not thy name on this my death-day, yet thou knowest verily that thou liest unto me."

He answered, "Sigurd am I called, and my father was Sigmund."

Says Fafnir, "Who egged thee on to this deed, and why wouldst thou be driven to it? Hadst thou never heard how that all folk were adrad of me, and of the awe of my countenance? But an eager father thou hadst, O bright-eyed swain!"

Sigurd answered, "A hardy heart urged me on hereto; and a strong hand and this sharp sword, which well thou knowest now, stood me in stead in the doing of the deed; *Seldom hath hardy eld a faint-heart youth.*"

Fafnir said, "Well, I wot that hadst thou waxed amid thy kin, thou mightest have good skill to slay folk in thine anger; but more of a marvel is it, that thou, a bondsman taken in war, shouldst have the heart to set on me, *for few among bondsmen have heart for the fight.*"

Said Sigurd, "Wilt thou then cast it in my teeth that I am far away from my kin? Albeit I was a bondsman, yet was I never shackled. God wot thou hast found me free enow."

Fafnir answered, "In angry wise dost thou take my speech; but hearken, for that same gold which I have owned shall be thy bane too."

Quoth Sigurd, "Fain would we keep all our wealth till that day of days; yet shall each man die once for all."

Said Fafnir, "Few things wilt thou do after my counsel; but take heed that thou shalt be drowned if thou farest unwarily over the sea; so bide thou rather on the dry land, for the coming of the calm tide."

Then said Sigurd, "Speak, Fafnir, and say, if thou art so exceeding wise, who are the Norns who rule the lot of all mothers' sons."

Fafnir answers, "Many there be and wide apart; for some are of the kin of the Æsir, and some are of Elfin kin, and some there are who are daughters of Dvalin."

Said Sigurd, "How namest thou the holm whereon Surt and the Æsir mix and mingle the water of the sword?"

"Unshapen is that holm hight," said Fafnir.

And yet again he said, "Regin, my brother, has brought about my end, and it gladdens my heart that thine too he bringeth about; for thus will things be according to his will."

And once again he spake, "A countenance of terror I bore up before all folk, after that I brooded over the heritage of my brother, and on every side did I spout out poison, so that none durst come anigh me, and of no weapon was I adrad, nor ever had I so many men before me, as that I deemed myself not stronger than all; for all men were sore afeard of me."

Sigurd answered and said, "Few may have victory by means of that same countenance of terror, for whoso comes amongst many shall one day find that no one man is by so far the mightiest of all."

Then says Fafnir, "Such counsel I give thee, that thou take thy horse and ride away at thy speediest, for ofttimes it falls out so, that he who gets a death-wound avenges himself none the less."

Sigurd answered, "Such as thy redes are I will nowise do

after them; nay, I will ride now to thy lair and take to me that great treasure of thy kin."

"Ride there then," said Fafnir, "and thou shalt find gold enow to suffice thee for all thy life-days; yet shall that gold be thy bane, and the bane of every one soever who owns it."

Then up stood Sigurd, and said, "Home would I ride and lose all that wealth, if I deemed that by the losing thereof I should never die; but every brave and true man will fain have his hand on wealth till that last day; but thou, Fafnir, wallow in the death-pain till Death and Hell have thee."

And therewithal Fafnir died.

Chapter 19

Of the Slaying of Regin, Son of Hreidmar

THEREAFTER CAME Regin to Sigurd, and said, "Hail, lord and master, a noble victory hast thou won in the slaying of Fafnir, whereas none durst heretofore abide in the path of him; and now shall this deed of fame be of renown while the world stands fast."

Then stood Regin staring on the earth a long while, and presently thereafter spake from heavy mood: "Mine own brother hast thou slain, and scarce may I be called sackless of the deed."

Then Sigurd tok his sword Gram and dried it on the earth, and spake to Regin—

"Afar thou faredst when I wrought this deed and tried this sharp sword with the hand and the might of me; with all the might and main of a dragon must I strive, while thou wert laid alow in the heather-bush, wotting not if it were earth or heaven."

Said Regin, "Long might this worm have lain in his lair, if the sharp sword I forged with my hand had not been good at need to thee; had that not been, neither thou nor any man would have prevailed against him as at this time."

Sigurd answers, "Whenas men meet foes in fight, better is stout heart than sharp sword."

Then said Regin, exceeding heavily, "Thou hast slain my brother, and scarce may I be sackless of the deed."

Therewith Sigurd cut out the heart of the worm with the sword called Ridil; but Regin drank of Fafnir's blood, and spake, "Grant me a boon, and do a thing little for thee to do. Bear the heart to the fire, and roast it, and give me thereof to eat."

Then Sigurd went his ways and roasted it on a rod; and when the blood bubbled out he laid his finger thereon to essay it, if it were fully done; and then he set his finger in his mouth, and lo, when the heart-blood of the worm touched his tongue, straightway he knew the voice of all fowls, and heard withal how the wood-peckers chattered in the brake beside him—

"There sittest thou, Sigurd, roasting Fafnir's heart for another, that thou shouldest eat thine ownself, and then thou shouldest become the wisest of all men."

And another spake: "There lies Regin, minded to beguile the man who trusts in him."

But yet again said the third, "Let him smite the head from off him then, and be only lord of all that gold."

And once more the fourth spake and said, "Ah, the wiser were he if he followed after that good counsel, and rode thereafter to Fafnir's lair, and took to him that mighty treasure that lieth there, and then rode over Hindfell, whereas sleeps Brynhild; for there would he get great wisdom. Ah, wise he were, if he did after your redes, and bethought him of his own weal; *for where wolf's ears are, wolf's teeth are near.*"

Then cried the fifth: "Yea, yea, not so wise is he as I deem him, if he spareth him, whose brother he hath slain already."

At last spake the sixth: "Handy and good rede to slay him, and be lord of the treasure!"

Then said Sigurd, "The time is unborn wherein Regin shall be my bane; nay, rather one road shall both these brothers fare."

And therewith he drew his sword Gram and struck off Regin's head.

Then heard Sigurd the wood-peckers a-singing, even as the song says.

For the first sang:

> Bind thou, Sigurd,
> The bright red rings!

> Not meet it is
> Many things to fear.
> A fair may know I,
> Fair of all the fairest
> Girt about with gold,
> Good for thy getting.

And the second:

> Green go the ways
> Toward the hall of Giuki
> That the fates show forth
> To those who fare thither;
> There the rich king
> Reareth a daughter;
> Thou shalt deal, Sigurd,
> With gold for thy sweetling.

And the third:

> A high hall is there
> Reared upon Hindfell,
> Without all around it
> Sweeps the red flame aloft
> Wise men wrought
> That wonder of halls
> With the unhidden gleam
> Of the glory of gold.

Then the fourth sang:

> Soft on the fell
> A shield-may sleepeth
> The lime-trees' red plague
> Playing about her:
> The sleep-thorn set Odin
> Into that maiden
> For her choosing in war
> The one he willed not.

> Go, son, behold
> That may under helm

Whom from battle
Vinskornir bore,
From her may not turn
The torment of sleep.
Dear offspring of kings
In the dread Norns' despite.

Then Sigmund ate some deal of Fafnir's heart, and the remnant he kept. Then he leapt on his horse and rode along the trail of the worm Fafnir, and so right unto his abiding-place; and he found it open, and beheld all the doors and the gear of them that they were wrought of iron: yea, and all the beams of the house; and it was dug down deep into the earth: there found Sigurd gold exceeding plenteous, and the sword Rotti; and thence he took the Helm of Awe, and the Gold Byrny, and many things fair and good. So much gold he found there, that he thought verily that scarce might two horses, or three belike, bear it thence. So he took all the gold and laid it in two great chests, and set them on the horse Grani, and took the reins of him, but nowise will he stir, neither will he abide smiting. Then Sigurd knows the mind of the horse, and leaps on the back of him, and smites and spurs into him, and off the horse goes even as if he were unladen.

Chapter 20

Of Sigurd's Meeting with Brynhild on the Mountain

BY LONG roads rides Sigurd, till he comes at the last up on to
Hindfell, and wends his way south to the land of the Franks;
and he sees before him on the fell a great light, as of fire burning, and flaming up even unto the heavens; and when he came
thereto, lo, a shield-hung castle before him, and a banner on
the topmost thereof: into the castle went Sigurd, and saw one
lying there asleep, and all-armed. Therewith he takes the helm
from off the head of him, and sees that it is no man, but a
woman; and she was clad in a byrny as closely set on her as
though it had grown to her flesh; so he rent it from the collar
downwards; and then the sleeves thereof, and ever the sword
bit on it as if it were cloth. Then said Sigurd that over-long
had she lain asleep; but she asked—

"What thing of great might is it that has prevailed to rend
my byrny, and draw me from my sleep?"

Even as sings the song—

> What bit on the byrny,
> Why breaks my sleep away,
> Who has turned from me
> My wan tormenting?

"Ah, it is so, that here is come Sigurd Sigmundson, bearing

149

Fafnir's helm on his head and Fafnir's bane in his hand?"

Then answered Sigurd—

> "Sigmund's son
> With Sigurd's sword
> E'en now rent down
> The raven's wall.

"Of the Volsung's kin is he who has done the deed; but now I have heard that thou art daughter of a mighty king, and folk have told us that thou wert lovely and full of lore, and now I will try the same."

Then Brynhild sang—

> "Long have I slept
> And slumbered long,
> Many and long are the woes of mankind,
> By the might of Odin
> Must I bide helpless
> To shake from off me the spells of slumber.

> Hail to the day come back!
> Hail, sons of the daylight!
> Hail to thee, dark night, and thy daughter!
> Look with kind eyes a-down,
> On us sitting here lonely,
> And give unto us the gain that we long for.

> Hail to the Æsir,
> And the sweet Asyniur!
> Hail to the fair earth fulfilled of plenty!
> Fair words, wise hearts,
> Would we win from you,
> And healing hands while life we hold."

Then Brynhild speaks again and says, "Two kings fought, one hight Helm Gunnar, an old man, and the greatest of warriors, and Odin had promised the victory unto him; but his foe was Agnar, or Audi's brother: and so I smote down Helm Gunnar in the fight; and Odin, in vengeance for that deed, stuck the sleep-thorn into me, and said that I should never again have the victory, but should be given away in marriage; but there-against I vowed a vow, that never would I wed one who knew the name of fear."

Then said Sigurd, "Teach us the lore of mighty matters!"

She said, "Belike thou cannest more skill in all than I; yet will I teach thee; yea, and with thanks, if there be aught of my cunning that will in anywise pleasure thee, either of runes or of other matters that are the root of things; but now let us drink together, and may the Gods give to us twain a good day, that thou mayst win good help and fame from my wisdom, and that thou mayst hereafter mind thee of that which we twain speak together."

Then Brynhild filled a beaker and bore it to Sigurd, and gave him the drink of love, and spake—

> "Beer bring I to thee,
>   Fair fruit of the byrnies' clash,
>   Mixed is it mightily,
>   Mingled with fame,
>   Brimming with bright lays
>   And pitiful runes,
>   Wise words, sweet words,
>   Speech of great game.
>
>   Runes of war know thou,
>   If great thou wilt be!
> Cut them on hilt of hardened sword,
>   Some of the brand's back,
>   Some on its shining side,
> Twice name Tyr therein.
>
>   Sea-runes good at need,
>   Learnt for ship's saving,
> For the good health of the swimming horse;
>   On the stern cut them,
>   Cut them on the rudder-blade
> And set flame to shaven oar:
>   Howso big be the sea-hills,
>   Howso blue beneath,
> Hail from the main then comest thou home.

Word-runes learn well
If thou wilt that no man
Pay back grief for the grief thou gavest;
  Wind thou these,
  Weave thou these,
Cast thou these all about thee,
  At the Thing,
  Where folk throng,
Unto the full doom faring.

Of ale-runes know the wisdom
If thou wilt that another's wife
Should not bewray thine heart that trusteth:
  Cut them on the mead-horn,
  On the back of each hand,
And nick an N upon thy nail.

Ale have thou heed
To sign from all harm
Leek lay thou in the liquor,
  Then I know for sure
  Never cometh to thee,
Mead with hurtful matters mingled.

Help-runes shalt thou gather
If skill thou wouldst gain
To loosen child from low-laid mother;
  Cut be they in hands hollow,
  Wrapped the joints round about;
Call for the Good-folks' gainsome helping.

Learn the bough-runes wisdom
If leech-lore thou lovest;
And wilt wot about wounds' searching
  On the bark be they scored;
  On the buds of trees
Whose boughs look eastward ever.

Thought-runes shalt thou deal with
If thou wilt be of all men

Fairest-souled wight, and wisest,
   These areded
   These first cut
These first took to heart high Hropt.

   On the shield were they scored
   That stands before the shining God,
   On Early-waking's ear,
   On All-knowing's hoof,
   On the wheel which runneth
   Under Rognir's chariot;
   On Sleipnir's jaw-teeth,
   On the sleigh's traces.

   On the rough bear's paws,
   And on Bragi's tongue,
   On the wolf's claws,
   And on eagle's bill,
   On bloody wings,
   And bridge's end;
   On loosing palms,
   And pity's path:

   On glass, and on gold,
   And on goodly silver,
   In wine and in wort,
   And the seat of the witch-wife;
   On Gungnir's point,
   And Grani's bosom;
   On the Norn's nail,
   And the neb of the night-owl.

   All these so cut,
   Were shaven and sheared,
And mingled in with holy mead,
And sent upon wide ways enow;
   Some abide with the Elves,
   Some abide with the Æsir,
Or with the wise Vanir,
Some still hold the sons of mankind.

These be the book-runes,
  And the runes of good help,
And all the ale-runes,
And the runes of much might;
  To whomso they may avail,
  Unbewildered unspoilt;
They are wholesome to have:
Thrive thou with these then.
When thou hast learnt their lore,
Till the Gods end thy life-days.

Now shalt thou choose thee
  E'en as choice is bidden,
Sharp steel's root and stem,
  Choose song or silence;
  See to each in thy heart,
All hurt has been heeded."

Then answered Sigurd—

"Ne'er shall I flee,
  Though thou wottest me fey;
Never was I born for blenching,
Thy love rede will I
  Hold aright in my heart
Even as long as I may live."

Chapter 21

More Wise Words of Brynhild

SIGURD SPAKE now, "Sure no wiser woman than thou art one may be found in the wide world; yea, yea, teach me more yet of thy wisdom!"

She answers, "Seemly is it that I do according to thy will, and show thee forth more redes of great avail, for thy prayer's sake and thy wisdom;" and she spake withal—

"Be kindly to friend and kin, and reward not their trespasses against thee; bear and forbear, and win for thee thereby long enduring praise of men.

"Take good heed of evil things: a may's love, and a man's wife; full oft thereof doth ill befall!

"Let not thy mind be overmuch crossed by unwise men at thronged meetings of folk; for oft these speak worse than they wot of; lest thou be called a dastard, and art minded to think that thou art even as is said; slay such an one on another day, and so reward his ugly talk.

"If thou farest by the way whereas bide evil things, be well ware of thyself; take not harbour near the highway though thou be benighted, for oft abide there ill wights for men's bewilderment.

"Let not fair women beguile thee, such as thou mayst meet at the feast, so that the thought thereof stand thee in stead of sleep, and a quiet mind; yea, draw them not to thee with kisses or other sweet things of love.

"If thou hearest the fool's word of a drunken man, strive not with him being drunk with drink and witless; many a grief, yea, and the very death, groweth from out such things.

"Fight thy foes in the field, nor be burnt in thine house.

"Never swear thou wrongsome oath; great and grim is the reward for the breaking of plighted troth.

"Give kind heed to dead men,—sick-dead, sea-dead, or sword-dead; deal heedfully with their dead corpses.

"Trow never in him for whom thou hast slain father, brother, or whatso near kin, yea, though young he be; *for oft waxes wolf in youngling.*

"Look thou with good heed to the wiles of thy friends; but little skill is given to me, that I should foresee the ways of thy life; yet good it were that hate fell not on thee from those of thy wife's house."

Sigurd spake, "None among the sons of men can be found wiser than thou; and thereby swear I, that thee will I have as my own, for near to my heart thou liest."

She answers, "Thee would I fainest choose, though I had all men's sons to choose from."

And thereto they plighted troth both of them.

Chapter 22

Of the Semblance and Array of Sigurd Fafnir's-bane

Now SIGURD rides away; many-folded is his shield, and blazing with red gold, and the image of a dragon is drawn thereon; and this same was dark brown above, and bright red below; and with even such-like image was adorned helm, and saddle, and coat-armour; and he was clad in the golden byrny, and all his weapons were gold-wrought.

Now for this cause was the drake drawn on all his weapons, that when he was seen of men, all folk might know who went there; yea, all those who had heard of his slaying of that great dragon, that the Vœrings call Fafnir; and for that cause are his weapons gold-wrought, and brown of hue, and that he was by far above other men in courtesy and goodly manners, and well-nigh in all things else; and whenas folk tell of all the mightiest champions, and the noblest chiefs, then ever is he named the foremost, and his name goes wide about on all tongues north of the sea of the Greek-lands, and even so shall it be while the world endures.

Now the hair of this Sigurd was golden-red of hue, fair of fashion, and falling down in great locks; thick and short was his beard, and of no other colour; high-nosed he was, broad and high-boned of face; so keen were his eyes, that few durst gaze up under the brows of him; his shoulders were as broad to look on as the shoulders of two; most duly was his body fashioned betwixt height and breadth, and in such wise as was seemliest; and this is the sign told of his height, that when he was girt with his sword Gram, which same was seven spans long, as he went through the full-grown rye-fields, the dew-shoe of the said sword smote the ears of the standing corn; and, for all that, greater was his strength than his growth: well could he wield sword, and cast forth spear, shoot shaft, and hold shield, bend bow, back horse, and do all the goodly deeds that he learned in his youth's days.

Wise he was to know things yet undone; and the voice of all fowls he knew, wherefore few things fell on him unawares.

Of many words he was, and so fair of speech withal, that whensoever he made it his business to speak, he never left speaking before that to all men it seemed full sure, that no otherwise must the matter be than as he said.

His sport and pleasure it was to give aid to his own folk, and to prove himself in mighty matters, to take wealth from his unfriends, and give the same to his friends.

Never did he lose heart, and of naught was he adrad.

Chapter 23

Sigurd comes to Hlymdale

FORTH SIGURD rides till he comes to a great and goodly dwelling, the lord whereof was a mighty chief called Heimir; he had to wife a sister of Brynhild, who was hight Bekkhild, because she had bidden at home, and learned handicraft, whereas Brynhild fared with helm and byrny unto the wars, wherefore was she called Brynhild.

Heimir and Bekkhild had a son called Alswid, the most courteous of men.

Now at this stead were men disporting them abroad, but when they see the man riding thereto, they leave their play to wonder at him, for none such had they ever seen erst; so they went to meet him, and gave him good welcome; Alswid bade him abide and have such things at his hands as he would; and he takes his bidding blithesomely; due service withal was established for him; four men bore the treasure of gold from off the horse, and the fifth took it to him to guard the same; therein were many things to behold, things of great price, and seldom seen; and great game and joy men had to look on byrnies and helms, and mighty rings, and wondrous great golden stoups, and all kinds of war weapons.

So there dwelt Sigurd long in great honour holden; and tidings of that deed of fame spread wide through all lands, of how he had slain that hideous and fearful dragon. So good joyance had they there together, and each was leal to other; and their sport was in the arraying of their weapons, and the shafting of their arrows, and the flying of their falcons.

Chapter 24

Sigurd sees Brynhild at Hlymdale

IN THOSE days came home to Heimir, Brynhild, his foster-daughter, and she sat in her bower with her maidens, and could more skill in handycraft than other women; she sat, overlaying cloth with gold, and sewing therein the great deeds which Sigurd had wrought, the slaying of the Worm, and the taking of the wealth of him, and the death of Regin withal.

Now tells the tale, that on a day Sigurd rode into the wood with hawk, and hound, and men thronging; and whenas he came home his hawk flew up to a high tower, and sat him down on a certain window. Then fared Sigurd after his hawk, and he saw where sat a fair woman, and knew that it was Brynhild, and he deems all things he sees there to be worthy together, both her fairness, and the fair things she wrought: and therewith he goes into the hall, but has no more joyance in the games of the men folk.

Then spake Alswid, "Why art thou so bare of bliss? this manner of thine grieveth us thy friends; why then wilt thou not hold to thy gleesome ways? Lo, thy hawks pine now, and thy horse Grani droops; and long will is be ere we are booted thereof?"

Sigurd answered, "Good friend, hearken to what lies on my mind; for my hawk flew up into a certain tower; and when I came thereto and took him, lo there I saw a fair woman, and she sat by a needlework of gold, and did thereon my deeds that are passed, and my deeds that are to come."

Then said Alswid, "Thou hast seen Brynhild, Budli's daughter, the greatest of great women."

"Yea, verily," said Sigurd; "but how came she hither?"

Alswid answered, "Short space there was betwixt the coming hither of the twain of you."

Says Sigurd, "Yea, but a few days agone I knew her for the best of the world's women."

Alswid said, "Give not all thine heed to one woman, being such a man as thou art; ill life to sit lamenting for what we may not have."

"I shall go meet her," says Sigurd, "and get from her love like my love, and give her a gold ring in token thereof."

Alswid answered, "None has ever yet been known whom she would let sit beside her, or to whom she would give drink; for ever will she hold to warfare and to the winning of all kinds of fame."

Sigurd said, "We know not for sure whether she will give us answer or not, or grant us a seat beside her."

So the next day after, Sigurd went to the bower, but Alswid stood outside the bower door, fitting shafts to his arrows.

Now Sigurd spake, "Abide, fair and hale lady,—how farest thou?"

She answered, "Well it fares; my kin and my friends live yet: but who shall say what goodhap folk may bear to their life's end?"

He sat him down by her, and there came in four damsels with great golden beakers, and the best of wine therein; and these stood before the twain.

Then said Brynhild, "This seat is for few, but and if my father come."

He answered, "Yet is it granted to one that likes me well."

Now that chamber was hung with the best and fairest of hangings, and the floor thereof was all covered with cloth.

Sigurd spake, "Now has it come to pass even as thou didst promise."

"O be thou welcome here!" said she, and arose therewith, and the four damsels with her, and bore the golden beaker to him, and bade him drink; he stretched out his hand to the beaker, and took it, and her hand withal, and drew her down beside him; and cast his arms round about her neck and kissed her, and said—

"Thou art the fairest that was ever born!"

But Brynhild said, "Ah, wiser is it not to cast faith and troth into a woman's power, for ever shall they break that they have promised."

He said, "That day would dawn the best of days over our heads whereon each of each should be made happy."

Brynhild answered, "It is not fated that we should abide together; I am a shield-may, and wear helm on head even as the kings of war, and them full oft I help, neither is the battle become loathsome to me."

Sigurd answered, "What fruit shall be of our life, if we live not together: harder to bear this pain that lies hereunder, than the stroke of sharp sword."

Brynhild answers, "I shall gaze on the hosts of the war-kings, but thou shalt wed Gudrun, the daughter of Giuki."

Sigurd answered, "What king's daughter lives to beguile me? neither am I double-hearted herein; and now I swear by the Gods that thee shall I have for mine own, or no woman else."

And even suchlike wise spake she.

Sigurd thanked her for her speech, and gave her a gold ring, and now they swore oath anew, and so he went his ways to his men, and is with them awhile in great bliss.

Chapter 25

Of the Dream of Gudrun, Giuki's Daughter

THERE WAS a king hight Giuki, who ruled a realm south of the Rhine; three sons he had, thus named: Gunnar, Hogni, and Guttorm, and Gudrun was the name of his daughter, the fairest of maidens; and all these children were far before all other king's children in all prowess, and in goodliness and growth withal; ever were his sons at the wars and wrought many a deed of fame. But Giuki had wedded Grimhild the Wise-wife.

Now Budli was the name of a king mightier than Giuki, mighty though they both were: and Atli was the brother of Brynhild: Atli was a fierce man and a grim, great and black to look on, yet noble of mien withal, and the greatest of warriors. Grimhild was a fierce-hearted woman.

Now the days of the Giukings bloomed fair, and chiefly because of those children, so far before the sons of men.

On a day Gudrun says to her mays that she may have no joy of heart; then a certain woman asked her wherefore her joy was departed.

She answered, "Grief came to me in my dreams, therefore is there sorrow in my heart, since thou must needs ask thereof."

"Tell it me, then, thy dream," said the woman, "for dreams oft forecast but the weather."

Gudrun answers, "Nay, nay, no weather is this; I dreamed that I had a fair hawk on my wrist, feathered with feathers of gold."

Says the woman, "Many have heard tell of thy beauty, thy wisdom, and thy courtesy; some king's son abides thee, then."

Gudrun answers, "I dreamed that naught was so dear to me as this hawk, and all my wealth had I cast aside rather than him."

The woman said, "Well, then, the man thou shalt have will be of the goodliest, and well shalt thou love him."

Gudrun answered, "It grieves me that I know not who he shall be; let us go seek Brynhild, for she belike will wot thereof."

So they arrayed them in gold and many a fair thing, and she went with her damsels till they came to the hall of Brynhild, and that hall was dight with gold, and stood on a high hill; and whenas their goings were seen, it was told Brynhild, that a company of women drove toward the burg in gilded waggons.

"That shall be Gudrun, Giuki's daughter," says she: "I dreamed of her last night; let us go meet her! no fairer woman may come to our house."

So they went abroad to meet them, and gave them good greeting, and they went into the goodly hall together; fairly painted it was within, and well adorned with silver vessel; cloths were spread under the feet of them, and all folk served them, and in many wise they sported.

But Gudrun was somewhat silent.

Then said Brynhild, "Ill to abash folk of their mirth; prithee do not so; let us talk together for our disport of mighty kings and their great deeds."

"Good talk," says Gudrun, "let us do even so; what kings deemest thou to have been the first of all men?"

Brynhild says, "The sons of Haki, and Hagbard withal; they brought to pass many a deed of fame in their warfare."

Gudrun answers, "Great men certes, and of noble fame! Yet Sigar took their one sister, and burned the other, house and all; and they may be called slow to revenge the deed; why didst thou not name my brethren, who are held to be the first of men as at this time?"

Brynhild says, "Men of good hope are they surely, though but little proven hitherto; but one I know far before them, Sigurd, the son of Sigmund the king; a youngling was he in the days when he slew the sons of Hunding, and revenged his father, and Eylimi, his mother's father."

Said Gudrun, "By what token tellest thou that?"

Brynhild answered, "His mother went amid the dead, and found Sigmund the king sore wounded, and would bind up his hurts; but he said he grew over old for war, and bade her lay this comfort to her heart, that she should bear the most famed of sons; and wise was the wise man's word therein: for after the death of King Sigmund, she went to King Alf, and there was Sigurd nourished in great honour, and day by day he wrought some deed of fame, and is the man most renowned of all the wide world."

Gudrun says, "From love hast thou gained these tidings of him; but for this cause came I here, to tell thee dreams of mine which have brought me great grief."

Says Brynhild, "Let not such matters sadden thee; abide with thy friends who wish thee blithesome, all of them!"

"This I dreamed," said Gudrun, "that we went, a many of us in company, from the bower, and we saw an exceeding great hart, that far excelled all other deer ever seen, and the hair of him was golden; and this deer we were all fain to take, but I alone got him; and he seemed to me better than all things else; but sithence thou, Brynhild, didst shoot and slay my deer even at my very knees, and such grief was that to me that scarce might I bear it; and then afterwards thou gavest me a wolf-cub, which besprinkled me with the blood of my brethren."

Brynhild answers, "I will arede thy dream, even as things shall come to pass hereafter; for Sigurd shall come to thee, even he whom I have chosen for my well-beloved; and Grimhild shall give him mead mingled with hurtful things, which shall cast us all into mighty strife. Him shalt thou have, and him shalt thou quickly miss; and Atli the king shalt thou wed;

and thy brethren shalt thou lose, and slay Atli withal in the end."

Gudrun answers, "Grief and woe to know that such things shall be!"

And therewith she and hers get them gone home to King Giuki.

Chapter 26

Sigurd comes to the Giukings and is wedded to Gudrun

NOW SIGURD goes his ways with all that great treasure, and in friendly wise he departs from them; and on Grani he rides with all his war-gear and the burden withal; and thus he rides until he comes to the hall of King Giuki; there he rides into the burg, and that sees one of the king's men, and he spake withal—

"Sure it may be deemed that here is come one of the Gods, for his array is all done with gold, and his horse is far mightier than other horses, and the manner of his weapons is most exceeding goodly, and most of all the man himself far excels all other men ever seen."

So the king goes out with his court and greets the man, and asks—

"Who art thou who thus ridest into my burg, as none has durst hitherto without the leave of my sons?"

He answered, "I am called Sigurd, son of King Sigmund."

Then said King Giuki, "Be thou welcome here then, and take at our hands whatso thou willest."

So he went into the king's hall, and all men seemed little beside him, and all men served him, and there he abode in great joyance.

Now oft they all ride abroad together, Sigurd and Gunnar

and Hogni, and ever is Sigurd far the foremost of them, mighty men of their hands though they were.

But Grimhild finds how heartily Sigurd loved Brynhild, and how oft he talks of her; and she falls to thinking how well it were, if he might abide there and wed the daughter of King Giuki, for she saw that none might come anigh to his goodliness, and what faith and goodhelp there was in him, and how that he had more wealth withal than folk might tell of any man; and the king did to him even as unto his own sons, and they for their parts held him of more worth than themselves.

So on a night as they sat at the drink, the queen arose, and went before Sigurd, and said—

"Great joy we have in thine abiding here, and all good things will we put before thee to take of us; lo now, take this horn and drink thereof."

So he took it and drank, and therewithal she said, "Thy father shall be Giuki the king, and I shall be thy mother, and Gunnar and Hogni shall be thy brethren, and all this shall be sworn with oaths each to each; and then surely shall the like of you never be found on earth."

Sigurd took her speech well, for with the drinking of that drink all memory of Brynhild departed from him. So there he abode awhile.

And on a day went Grimhild to Giuki the king, and cast her arms about his neck, and spake—

"Behold, there has now come to us the greatest of great hearts that the world holds; and needs must he be trusty and of great avail; give him thy daughter then, with plenteous wealth, and as much of rule as he will; perchance thereby he will be well content to abide here ever."

The king answered, "Seldom does it befall that kings offer their daughters to any; yet in higher wise will it be done to offer her to this man, than to take lowly prayers for her from others."

On a night Gudrun pours out the drink, and Sigurd beholds her how fair she is and how full of all courtesy.

Five seasons Sigurd abode there, and ever they passed their days together in good honour and friendship.

And so it befell that the kings held talk together, and Giuki said—

"Great good thou givest us, Sigurd, and with exceeding strength thou strengthenest our realm."

Then Gunnar said, "All things that may be will we do for thee, so thou abidest here long; both dominion shalt thou have, and our sister freely and unprayed for, whom another man would not get for all his prayers."

Sigurd says, "Thanks have ye for this wherewith ye honour me, and gladly will I take the same."

Therewith they swore brotherhood together, and to be even as if they were children of one father and one mother; and a noble feast was holden, and endured many days, and Sigurd drank at the wedding of him and Gudrun; and there might men behold all manner of game and glee, and each day the feast better and better.

Now fare these folk wide over the world, and do many great deeds, and slay many kings' sons, and no man has ever done such works of prowess as did they; then home they come again with much wealth won in war.

Sigurd gave of the serpent's heart to Gudrun, and she ate thereof, and became greater-hearted, and wiser than ere before: and the son of these twain was called Sigmund.

Now on a time went Grimhild to Gunnar her son, and spake—

"Fair blooms the life and fortune of thee, but for one thing only, and namely whereas thou art unwedded; go woo Brynhild; good rede is this, and Sigurd will ride with thee."

Gunnar answered, "Fair is she certes, and I am fain enow to win her;" and therewith he tells his father, and his brethren, and Sigurd, and they all prick him on to that wooing.

Chapter 27

The Wooing of Brynhild

NOW THEY array them joyously for their journey, and ride over hill and dale to the house of King Budli, and woo his daughter of him; in a good wise he took their speech, if so be that she herself would not deny them; but he said withal that so high-minded was she, that that man only might wed her whom she would.

Then they ride to Hlymdale, and there Heimir gave them good welcome; so Gunnar tells his errand; Heimir says, that she must needs wed but him whom she herself chose freely; and tells them how her abode was but a little way thence, and that he deemed that him only would she have who should ride through the flaming fire that was drawn round about her hall; so they depart and come to the hall and the fire, and see there a castle with a golden roof-ridge, and all round about a fire roaring up.

Now Gunnar rode on Goti, but Hogni on Holkvi, and Gunnar smote his horse to face the fire, but he shrank aback.

Then said Sigurd, "Why givest thou back, Gunnar?"

He answered, "The horse will not tread this fire; but lend me thy horse Grani."

"Yea, with all my good will," says Sigurd.

Then Gunnar rides him at the fire, and yet nowise will Grani stir, nor may Gunnar any the more ride through that fire. So now they change semblance, Gunnar and Sigurd, even as Grimhild had taught them; then Sigurd in the likeness of Gunnar mounts and rides, Gram in his hand, and golden spurs on his heels; then leapt Grani into the fire when he felt the spurs; and a mighty roar arose as the fire burned ever madder, and the earth trembled, and the flames went up even unto the heavens, nor had any dared to ride as he rode, even as it were through the deep mirk.

But now the fire sank withal, and he leapt from his horse and went into the hall, even as the song says—

> The flame flared at its maddest,
> Earth's fields fell a-quaking
> As the red flame aloft
> Licked the lowest of heaven.
> Few had been fain,
> Of the rulers of folk,
> To ride through that flame,
> Or athwart it to tread.
>
> Then Sigurd smote
> Grani with sword,
> And the flame was slaked
> Before the king;
> Low lay the flames
> Before the fain of fame;
> Bright gleamed the array
> That Regin erst owned.

Now when Sigurd had passed through the fire, he came into a certain fair dwelling, and therein sat Brynhild.

She asked, "What man is it?"

Then he named himself Gunnar, son of Giuki, and said— "Thou art awarded to me as my wife, by the good-will and word of thy father and thy foster-father, and I have ridden through the flames of thy fire, according to thy word that thou hast set forth."

"I wot not clearly," she said, "how I shall answer thee."

Now Sigurd stood upright on the hall floor, and leaned on the hilt of his sword, and he spake to Brynhild—

"In reward thereof, shall I pay thee a great dower in gold and goodly things?"

She answered in heavy mood from her seat, whereas she sat like unto swan on billow, having a sword in her hand, and a helm on her head, and being clad in a byrny, "O Gunnar," she says, "speak not to me of such things; unless thou be the first and best of all men; for then shalt thou slay those my wooers, if thou hast heart thereto; I have been in battles with the king of the Greeks, and our weapons were stained with red blood, and for such things still I yearn."

He answered, "Yea, certes many great deeds hast thou done; but yet call thou to mind thine oath, concerning the riding through of this fire, wherein thou didst swear that thou wouldst go with the man who should do this deed."

So she found that he spake but the sooth, and she paid heed to his words, and arose, and greeted him meetly, and he abode there three nights, and they lay in one bed together; but he took the sword Gram and laid it betwixt them: then she asked him why he laid it there; and he answered, that in that wise must he needs wed his wife or else get his bane.

Then she took from off her the ring Andvari's-loom, which he had given her aforetime, and gave it to him, but he gave her another ring out of Fafnir's hoard.

Thereafter he rode away through the same fire unto his fellows, and he and Gunnar changed semblances again, and rode unto Hlymdale, and told how it had gone with them.

That same day went Brynhild home to her foster-father, and tells him as one whom she trusted, how that there had come a king to her; "And he rode through my flaming fire, and said he was come to woo me, and named himself Gunnar; but I said that such a deed might Sigurd alone have done, with whom I plighted troth on the mountain; and he is my first troth-plight, and my well-beloved."

Heimir said that things must needs abide even as now they had now come to pass.

Brynhild said, "Aslaug the daughter of me and Sigurd shall be nourished here with thee."

Now the kings fare home, but Brynhild goes to her father; Grimhild welcomes the kings meetly, and thanks Sigurd for his fellowship; and withal is a great feast made, and many were the guests thereat; and thither came Budli the King with his daughter Brynhild, and his son Atli, and for many days did the feast endure: and at that feast was Gunnar wedded to Brynhild: but when it was brought to an end, once more has Sigurd memory of all the oaths that he sware unto Brynhild, yet withal he let all things abide in rest and peace."

Brynhild and Gunnar sat together in great game and glee, and drank goodly wine.

Chapter 28

How the Queens held angry converse together at the Bathing

ON A DAY as the Queens went to the river to bathe them, Brynhild waded the farthest out into the river; then asked Gudrun what that deed might signify.

Brynhild said, "Yea, and why then should I be equal to thee in this matter more than in others? I am minded to think that my father is mightier than thine, and my true-love has wrought many wondrous works of fame, and hath ridden the flaming fire withal, while thy husband was but the thrall of King Hjalprek."

Gudrun answered full of wrath, "Thou wouldst be wise if thou shouldst hold thy peace rather than revile my husband: lo now, the talk of all men it is, that none has ever abode in this world like unto him in all matters soever; and little it beseems thee of all folk to mock him who was thy first beloved: and Fafnir he slew, yea, and he rode thy flaming fire, whereas thou didst deem that he was Gunnar the King, and by thy side he lay, and took from thine hand the ring Andvari's-loom;— here mayst thou well behold it!"

Then Brynhild saw the ring and knew it, and waxed as wan as a dead woman, and she went home and spake no word the evening long.

So when Sigurd came to bed to Gudrun she asked him why Brynhild's joy was so departed.

He answered, "I know not, but sore I misdoubt me that soon we shall know thereof overwell."

Gudrun said, "Why may she not love her life, having wealth and bliss, and the praise of all men, and the man withal that she would have?"

"Ah, yea!" said Sigurd, "and where in all the world was she then, when she said that she deemed she had the noblest of all men, and the dearest to her heart of all?"

Gudrun answers, "Tomorn will I ask her concerning this, who is the liefest to her of all men for a husband."

Sigurd said, "Needs must I forbid thee this, and full surely wilt thou rue the deed if thou doest it."

Now the next morning they sat in the bower, and Brynhild was silent; then spake Gudrun—

"Be merry, Brynhild! Grievest thou because of that speech of ours together, or what other thing slayeth thy bliss?"

Brynhild answers, "With naught but evil intent thou sayest this, for a cruel heart thou hast."

"Say not so," said Gudrun; "but rather tell me all the tale."

Brynhild answers, "Ask such things only as are good for thee to know—matters meet for mighty dames. Good to love good things when all goes according to thy heart's desire!"

Gudrun says, "Early days for me to glory in that; but this word of thine looketh toward some foreseeing. What ill dost thou thrust at us? I did naught to grieve thee."

Brynhild answers, "For this shalt thou pay, in that thou hast got Sigurd to thee,—nowise can I see thee living in the bliss thereof, whereas thou hast him, and the wealth and the might of him."

But Gudrun answered, "Naught knew I of your words and vows together; and well might my father look to the mating of me without dealing with thee first."

"No secret speech had we," quoth Brynhild, "though we swore oath together; and full well didst thou know that thou wentest about to beguile me; verily thou shalt have thy reward!"

Says Gudrun, "Thou art mated better than thou art worthy of; but thy pride and rage shall be hard to slake belike, and therefor shall many a man pay."

"Ah, I should be well content," said Brynhild, "if thou hadst not the nobler man!"

Gudrun answers, "So noble a husband hast thou, that who knows of a greater king or a lord of more wealth and might?"

Says Brynhild, "Sigurd slew Fafnir, and that only deed is of more worth than all the might of King Gunnar."

(Even as the song says):

> The worm Sigurd slew,
> Nor ere shall that deed
> Be worsened by age
> While the world is alive:
> But thy brother the King
> Never durst, never bore
> The flame to ride down
> Through the fire to fare.

Gudrun answers, "Grani would not abide the fire under Gunnar the King, but Sigurd durst the deed, and thy heart may well abide without mocking him."

Brynhild answers, "Nowise will I hide from thee that I deem no good of Grimhild."

Says Gudrun, "Nay, lay no ill words on her, for in all things she is to thee as to her own daughter."

"Ah," says Brynhild, "she is the beginning of all this bale that biteth so; an evil drink she bare to Sigurd, so that he had no more memory of my very name."

"All wrong thou talkest; a lie without measure is this," quoth Gudrun.

Brynhild answered, "Have thou joy of Sigurd according to the measure of the wiles wherewith ye have beguiled me! unworthily have ye conspired against me; may all things go with you as my heart hopes!"

Gudrun says, "More joy shall I have of him than thy wish would give unto me: but to no man's mind it came, that he had aforetime his pleasure of me; nay not once."

"Evil speech thou speakest," says Brynhild; "when thy wrath runs off thou wilt rue it; but come now, let us no more cast angry words one at the other!"

Says Gudrun, "Thou wert the first to cast such words at me, and now thou makest as if thou wouldst amend it, but a cruel and hard heart abides behind."

"Let us lay aside vain babble," says Brynhild. "Long did I hold my peace concerning my sorrow of heart, and, lo now, thy brother alone do I love; let us fall to other talk."

Gudrun said, "Far beyond all this doth thine heart look."

And so ugly ill befell from that going to the river, and that knowing of the ring, wherefrom did all their talk arise.

Chapter 29

Of Brynhild's Grief and Mourning

AFTER THIS talk Brynhild lay a-bed, and tidings were brought to King Gunnar that Brynhild was sick; he goes to see her thereon, and asks what ails her; but she answered him naught, but lay there as one dead: and when he was hard on her for an answer, she said—

"What didst thou with that ring that I gave thee, even the one which King Budli gave me at our last parting, when thou and King Giuki came to him and threatened fire and the sword, unless ye had me to wife? Yea, at that time he led me apart, and asked me which I had chosen of those who were come; but I prayed him that I might abide to ward the land and be chief over the third part of his men; then were there two choices for me to deal betwixt, either that I should be wedded to him whom he would, or lose all my weal and friendship at his hands; and he said withal that his friendship would be better to me than his wrath: then I bethought me whether I should yield to his will, or slay many a man; and therewithal I deemed that it would avail little to strive with him, and so it fell out, that I promised to wed whomsoever should ride the horse Grani with Fafnir's Hoard, and ride through my flaming fire, and slay those men whom I called on him to slay, and now so it was, that none durst ride, save Sigurd only, because he lacked no heart thereto; yea and the Worm he slew, and Regin, and five kings beside; but thou,

Gunnar, durst do naught; as pale as a dead man didst thou wax, and no king thou art, and no champion; so whereas I made a vow unto my father, that him alone would I love who was the noblest man alive, and that this is none save Sigurd, lo, now have I broken my oath and brought it to naught, since he is none of mine, and for this cause shall I compass thy death; and a great reward of evil things have I wherewith to reward Grimhild;—never, I wot, has woman lived eviler or of lesser heart than she."

Gunnar answered in such wise that few might hear him, "Many a vile word hast thou spoken, and an evil-hearted woman art thou, whereas thou revilest a woman far better than thou; never would she curse her life as thou dost; nay, nor has she tormented dead folk, or murdered any; but lives her life well praised of all."

Brynhild answered, "Never have I dwelt with evil things privily, or done loathsome deeds;—yet most fain I am to slay thee."

And therewith would she slay King Gunnar, but Hogni laid her in fetters; but then Gunnar spake withal—

"Nay, I will not that she abide in fetters."

Then said she, "Heed it not! for never again seest thou me glad in thine hall, never drinking, never at the chessplay, never speaking the words of kindness, never overlaying the fair cloths with gold, never giving thee good counsel;—ah, my sorrow of heart that I might not get Sigurd to me!"

Then she sat up and smote her needlework, and rent it asunder, and bade set open her bower doors, that far away might the wailings of her sorrow be heard; then great mourning and lamentation there was, so that folk heard it far and wide through that abode.

Now Gudrun asked her bower-maidens why they sat so joyless and downcast. "What has come to you, that ye fare ye as witless women, or what unheard-of wonders have befallen you?"

Then answered a waiting lady, hight Swaflod, "An untimely, an evil day it is, and our hall is fulfilled of lamentation."

Then spake Gudrun to one of her handmaids, "Arise, for we have slept long; go, wake Brynhild, and let us fall to our needlework and be merry."

"Nay, nay," she says, "nowise may I wake her, or talk with her; for many days has she drunk neither mead nor wine; surely the wrath of the Gods has fallen upon her."

Then spake Gudrun to Gunnar, "Go and see her," she says, "and bid her know that I am grieved with her grief."

"Nay," says Gunnar, "I am forbid to go see her or to share her weal."

Nevertheless he went unto her, and strives in many wise to have speech of her, but gets no answer whatsoever: therefore he gets him gone and finds Hogni, and bids him go see her: he said he was loth thereto, but went, and gat no more of her.

Then they go and find Sigurd, and pray him to visit her; he answered naught thereto, and so matters abode for that night.

But the next day, when he came home from hunting, Sigurd went to Gudrun, and spake—

"In such wise do matters show to me, as though great and evil things will betide from this trouble and upheaving, and that Brynhild will surely die."

Gudrun answers, "O my lord, by great wonders is she encompassed, seven days and seven nights has she slept, and none has dared wake her."

"Nay, she sleeps not," said Sigurd, "her heart is dealing rather with dreadful intent against me."

Then said Gudrun, weeping, "Woe worth the while for thy death! go and see her; and wot if her fury may not be abated; give her gold, and smother up her grief and anger therewith!"

Then Sigurd went out, and found the door of Brynhild's chamber open; he deemed she slept, and drew the clothes from off her, and said—

"Awake, Brynhild! the sun shineth now over all the house, and thou hast slept enough; cast off grief from thee, and take up gladness!"

She said, "And how then hast thou dared to come to me? in this treason none was worse to me than thou."

Said Sigurd, "Why wilt thou not speak to folk? for what cause sorrowest thou?"

Brynhild answers, "Ah, to thee will I tell of my wrath!"

Sigurd said, "As one under a spell art thou, if thou deemest that there is aught cruel in my heart against thee; but thou hast him for husband whom thou didst choose."

"Ah, nay," she said, "never did Gunnar ride through the fire to me, nor did he give me to dower the host of the slain: I wondered at the man who came into my hall; for I deemed indeed that I knew thine eyes; but I might not see clearly, or divide the good from the evil, because of the veil that lay heavy on my fortune."

Says Sigurd, "No nobler men are there than the sons of Giuki, they slew the king of the Danes, and that great chief, the brother of King Budli."

Brynhild answered, "Surely for many an ill-deed must I reward them; mind me not of my griefs against them! But thou, Sigurd, slewest the Worm, and rodest the fire through; yea, and for my sake, and not one of the sons of King Giuki."

Sigurd answers, "I am not thy husband, and thou art not my wife; yet did a farfamed king pay dower to thee."

Says Brynhild, "Never looked I at Gunnar in such a wise that my heart smiled on him; and hard and fell am I to him, though I hide it from others."

"A marvellous thing," says Sigurd, "not to love such a king; what angers thee most? for surely his love should be better to thee than gold."

"This is the sorest sorrow to me," she said, "that the bitter sword is not reddened in thy blood."

"Have no fear thereof!" says he, "no long while to wait or the bitter sword stand deep in my heart; and no worse needest thou to pray for thyself, for thou wilt not live when I am dead; the days of our two lives shall be few enough from henceforth."

Brynhild answers, "Enough and to spare of bale is in thy speech, since thou bewrayedst me, and didst twin me and all bliss;—naught do I heed my life or death."

Sigurd answers, "Ah, live, and love King Gunnar and me withal! and all my wealth will I give thee if thou die not."

Brynhild answers, "Thou knowest me not, nor the heart that is in me; for thou art the first and best of all men, and I am become the most loathsome of all women to thee."

"This is truer," says Sigurd, "that I loved thee better than myself, though I fell into the wiles from whence our lives may not escape; for whenso my own heart and mind availed me, then I sorrowed sore that thou wert not my wife; but as I might I put my trouble from me, for in a king's dwelling was I; and withal and in spite of all I was well content that we were all together. Well may it be, that that shall come to pass which is foretold; neither shall I fear the fulfilment thereof."

Brynhild answered, and said, "Too late thou tellest me that my grief grieved thee: little pity shall I find now."

Sigurd said, "This my heart would, that thou and I should go into one bed together; even so wouldst thou be my wife."

Said Brynhild, "Such words may nowise be spoken, nor will I have two kings in one hall; I will lay my life down rather than beguile Gunnar the King."

And therewith she call to mind how they met, they two, on the mountain, and swore an oath each to each.

"But now is all changed, and I will not live."

"I might not call to mind thy name," said Sigurd, "or know thee again, before the time of thy wedding; the greatest of all griefs is that."

Then said Brynhild, "I swore an oath to wed the man who should ride my flaming fire, and that oath will I hold to, or die."

"Rather than thou die, I will wed thee, and put away Gudrun," said Sigurd.

But therewithal so swelled the heart betwixt the sides of him, that the rings of his byrny burst asunder.

"I will not have thee," says Brynhild, "nay, nor any other!"

Then Sigurd got him gone.

So saith the song of Sigurd—

> "Out then went Sigurd,
>   The great kings' well-loved,
> From the speech and the sorrow,
>   Sore drooping, so grieving,
> That the shirt round about him
>   Of iron rings woven,
> From the sides brake asunder
>   Of the brave in the battle."

So when Sigurd came into the hall, Gunnar asked if he had come to a knowledge of what great grief lay heavy on her, or if she had power of speech: and Sigurd said that she lacked it not. So now Gunnar goes to her again, and asked her, what wrought her woe, or if there were anything that might amend it.

"I will not live," says Brynhild, "for Sigurd has bewrayed me, yea, and thee no less, whereas thou didst suffer him to come into my bed: lo thou, two men in one dwelling I will not have; and this shall be Sigurd's death, or thy death, or my death;—for now has he told Gudrun all, and she is mocking me even now!"

Chapter 30

Of the Slaying of Sigurd Fafnir's-bane

THEREAFTER BRYNHILD went out, and sat under her bower-wall, and had many words of wailing to say, and still she cried that all things were loathsome to her, both land and lordship alike, so she might not have Sigurd.

But therewith came Gunnar to her yet again, and Brynhild spake, "Thou shalt lose both realm and wealth, and thy life and me, for I shall fare home to my kin, and abide there in sorrow, unless thou slayest Sigurd and his son; never nourish thou a wolfcub."

Gunnar grew sick at heart thereat, and might nowise see what fearful thing lay beneath it all; he was bound to Sigurd by oath, and this way and that way swung the heart within him; but at the last he bethought him of the measureless shame if his wife went from him, and he said within himself, "Brynhild is better to me than all things else, and the fairest woman of all women, and I will lay down my life rather than lose the love of her." And herewith he called to him his brother and spake,—

"Trouble is heavy on me," and he tells him that he must needs slay Sigurd, for that he has failed him where in he trusted him; "so let us be lords of the gold and the realm withal."

Hogni answers, "Ill it behoves us to break our oaths with wrack and wrong, and withal great aid we have in him; no

kings shall be as great as we, if so be the King of the Hun-folk
may live; such another brother-in-law never may we get again;
bethink thee how good it is to have such a brother-in-law, and
such sons to our sister! But well I see how things stand, for
this has Brynhild stirred thee up to, and surely shall her counsel drag us into huge shame and scathe."

Gunnar says, "Yet shall it be brought about: and, lo, a rede
thereto;—let us egg on our brother Guttorm to the deed; he is
young, and of little knowledge, and is clean out of all the oaths
moreover."

"Ah, set about in ill wise," says Hogni, "and though indeed
it may well be compassed, a due reward shall we gain for the
bewrayal of such a man as is Sigurd."

Gunnar says, "Sigurd shall die, or I shall die."

And therewith he bids Brynhild arise and be glad at heart:
so she arose, and still ever she said that Gunnar should come
no more into her bed till the deed was done.

So the brothers fall to talk, and Gunnar says that it is a
deed well worthy of death, that taking of Brynhild's maiden-
head; "So come now, let us prick on Guttorm to do the deed."

Therewith they call him to them, and offer him gold and
great dominion, as they well have might to do. Yea, and they
took a certain worm and somewhat of wolf's flesh and let
seethe them together, and gave him to eat of the same, even
as the singer sings—

> Fish of the wild-wood,
> Worm smooth crawling,
> With wolf-meat mingled,
> They minced for Guttorm;
> Then in the beaker,
> In the wine his mouth knew,
> They set it, still doing
> More deeds of wizards.

Wherefore with the eating of this meat he grew so wild and
eager, and with all things about him, and with the heavy words
of Grimhild, that he gave his word to do the deed; and mighty
honour they promised him in reward thereof.

But of these evil wiles naught at all knew Sigurd, for he

might not deal with his shapen fate, nor the measure of his life-days, neither deemed he that he was worthy of such things at their hands.

So Guttorm went in to Sigurd the next morning as he lay upon his bed, yet durst he not do aught against him, but shrank back out again; yea, and even so he fared a second time, for so bright and eager were the eyes of Sigurd that few durst look upon him. But the third time he went in, and there lay Sigurd asleep; then Guttorm drew his sword and thrust Sigurd through in such wise that the sword point smote into the bed beneath him; then Sigurd awoke with that wound, and Guttorm gat him unto the door; but therewith Sigurd caught up the sword Gram, and cast it after him, and it smote him on the back, and struck him asunder in the midst, so that the feet of him fell one way, and the head and hands back into the chamber.

Now Gudrun lay asleep on Sigurd's bosom, but she woke up unto woe that may not be told of, all swimming in the blood of him, and in such wise did she bewail her with weeping and words of sorrow, that Sigurd rose up on the bolster, and spake.

"Weep not," said he, "for thy brothers live for thy delight; but a young son have I, too young to be ware of his foes; and an ill turn have these played against their own fortune; for never will they get a mightier brother-in-law to ride abroad with them; nay, nor a better son to their sister, than this one, if he may grow to man's estate. Lo, now is that come to pass which was foretold me long ago, but from mine eyes has it been hidden, for none may fight against his fate and prevail. Behold this has Brynhild brought to pass, even she who loves me before all men; but this may I swear, that never have I wrought ill to Gunnar, but rather have ever held fast to my oath with him, nor was I ever too much a friend to his wife. And now if I had been forewarned, and had been afoot with my weapons, then should many a man have lost his life or ever I had fallen, and all those brethren should have been slain, and a harder work would the slaying of me have been than the slaying of the mightiest bull or the mightiest boar of the wild-wood."

And even therewithal life left the King; but Gudrun moaned

and drew a weary breath, and Brynhild heard it, and laughed when she heard her moaning.

Then said Gunnar, "Thou laughest not because thy heart-roots are gladdened, or else why doth thy visage wax so wan? Sure an evil creature thou art; most like thou art nigh to thy death! Lo now, how meet would it be for thee to behold thy brother Atli slain before thine eyes, and that thou shouldst stand over him dead; whereas we must needs now stand over our brother-in-law in such a case—our brother-in-law and our brother's bane."

She answered, "None need mock at the measure of slaughter being unfulfilled; yet heedeth not Atli your wrath or your threats; yea, he shall live longer than ye, and be a mightier man."

Hogni spake and said, "Now hath come to pass the sooth-saying of Brynhild; an ill work not to be atoned for."

And Gudrun said, "My kinsmen have slain my husband; but ye, when ye next ride to the war and are come into the battle, then shall ye look about and see that Sigurd is neither on the right hand nor the left, and ye shall know that he was your good-hap and your strength; and if he had lived and had sons, then should ye have been strengthened by his offspring and his kin."

Chapter 31

Of the Lamentation of Gudrun over Sigurd dead, as it is told in the ancient Songs

GUDRUN OF old days
Drew near to dying
As she sat in sorrow
Over Sigurd;
Yet she sighed not
Nor smote hand on hand,
Nor wailed she aught
As other women.

Then went earls to her,
Full of all wisdom,
Fain help to deal
To her dreadful heart:
Hushed was Gudrun
Of wail, or greeting,
But with a heavy woe
Was her heart a-breaking.

Bright and fair
Sat the great earls' brides,
Gold arrayed
Before Gudrun;

Each told the tale
Of her great trouble,
The bitterest bale
She erst abode

Then spake Giaflaug,
Giuki's sister:
"Lo upon earth
I live most loveless
Who of five mates
Must see the ending,
Of daughters twain
And three sisters,
Of brethren eight,
And abide behind lonely."

Naught gat Gudrun
Of wail and greeting,
So heavy was she
For her dead husband,
So dreadful-hearted
For the King laid dead there.

Then spake Herborg
Queen of Hunland—
"Crueller tale
Have I to tell of,
Of my seven sons
Down in the Southlands,
And the eighth man, my mate,
Felled in the death-mead.

"Father and mother,
And four brothers,
On the wide sea
The winds and death played with;
The billows beat
On the bulwark boards.

"Alone must I sing o'er them,
Alone must I array them,

Alone must my hands deal with
Their departing;
And all this was
In one season's wearing,
And none was left
For love or solace.

"Then was I bound
A prey of the battle,
When that same season
Wore to its ending;
As a tiring may
Must I bind the shoon
Of the duke's high dame,
Every day at dawning.

"From her jealous hate
Gat I heavy mocking,
Cruel lashes
She laid upon me,
Never met I
Better master
Or mistress worser
In all the wide world."

Naught gat Gudrun
Of wail or greeting,
So heavy was she
For her dead husband,
So dreadful-hearted
For the King laid dead there.

Then spake Gullrond,
Giuki's daughter
"O foster-mother,
Wise as thou mayst be,
Naught canst thou better
The young wife's bale."
And she bade uncover
The dead King's corpse.

She swept the sheet
Away from Sigurd,
And turned his cheek
Towards his wife's knees—
"Look on thy loved one
Lay lips to his lips,
E'en as thou wert clinging
To thy king alive yet!"

Once looked Gudrun—
One look only,
And saw her lord's locks
Lying all bloody,
The great man's eyes
Glazed and deadly,
And his heart's bulwark
Broken by sword-edge.

Back then sank Gudrun,
Back on the bolster,
Loosed was her head array,
Red did her cheeks grow,
And the rain-drops ran
Down over her knees.

Then wept Gudrun,
Giuki's daughter,
So that the tears flowed
Through the pillow;
As the geese withal
That were in the homefield,
The fair fowls the may owned,
Fell a-screaming.

Then spake Gullrond,
Giuki's daughter—
"Surely knew I
No love like your love
Among all men,
On the mould abiding;

Naught wouldst thou joy in
Without or within doors,
O my sister,
Save beside Sigurd."

Then spake Gudrun,
Giuki's daughter—
"Such was my Sigurd
Among the sons of Giuki,
As is the king leek
O'er the low grass waxing,
Or a bright stone
Strung on band,
Or a pearl of price
On a prince's brow.

"Once was I counted
By the king's warriors
Higher than any
Of Herjan's mays;
Now am I as little
As the leaf may be,
Amid wind-swept wood
Now when dead he lieth.

"I miss from my seat,
I miss from my bed,
My darling of sweet speech.
Wrought the sons of Giuki,
Wrought the sons of Giuki,
This sore sorrow,
Yea, for their sister,
Most sore sorrow.

"So may your lands
Lie waste on all sides,
As ye have broken
Your bounden oaths!

Ne'er shalt thou, Gunnar,
The gold have joy of,

The dear-bought rings
Shall drag thee to death,
Whereon thou swarest
Oath unto Sigurd.

"Ah, in the days by-gone
Great mirth in the homefield
When my Sigurd
Set saddle on Grani,
And they went their ways
For the wooing of Brynhild!
An ill day, an ill woman,
And most ill hap!"

Then spake Brynhild,
Budli's daughter—
"May the woman lack
Both love and children,
Who gained greeting
For thee, O Gudrun!
Who gave thee this morning
Many words!"

Then spake Gullrond,
Giuki's daughter—
"Hold peace of such words
Thou hated of all folk!
The bane of brave men
Hast thou been ever,
All waves of ill
Wash over thy mind,
To seven great kings
Hast thou been a sore sorrow,
And the death of good will
To wives and women."

Then spake Brynhild,
Budli's daughter—
"None but Atli

Brought bale upon us,
My very brother
Born of Budli.

"When we saw in the hall
Of the Hunnish people
The gold a-gleaming
On the kingly Giukings;
I have paid for that faring
Oft and full,
And for the sight
That then I saw."

By a pillar she stood
And strained its wood to her;
From the eyes of Brynhild,
Budli's daughter,
Flashed out fire,
And she snorted forth venom,
As the sore wounds she gazed on
Of the dead-slain Sigurd.

Chapter 32

Of the Ending of Brynhild

AND NOW none might know for what cause Brynhild must bewail with weeping for what she had prayed for with laughter: but she spake—

"Such a dream I had, Gunnar, as that my bed was acold, and that thou didst ride into the hands of thy foes: lo now, ill shall it go with thee and all thy kin, O ye breakers of oaths; for on the day thou slayedst him, dimly didst thou remember how thou didst blend thy blood with the blood of Sigurd, and with an ill reward hast thou rewarded him for all that he did well to thee; whereas he gave unto thee to be the mightiest of men; and well was it proven how fast he held to his oath sworn, when he came to me and laid betwixt us the sharp-edged sword that in venom had been made hard. All too soon did ye fall to working wrong against him and against me, whenas I abode at home with my father, and had all that I would, and had no will that any one of you should be any of mine, as ye rode into our garth, ye three kings together; but then Atli led me apart privily, and asked me if I would not have him who rode Grani;—yea, a man nowise like unto you; but in those days I plighted myself to the son of King Sigmund and no other; and lo, now, no better shall ye fare for the death of me."

Then rose up Gunnar, and laid his arms about her neck,

and besought her to live and have wealth from him; and all others in likewise letted her from dying; but she thrust them all from her, and said that it was not the part of any to let her in that which was her will.

Then Gunnar called to Hogni, and prayed him for counsel, and bade him go to her, and see if he might perchance soften her dreadful heart, saying withal, that now they had need enough on their hands in the slaking of her grief, till time might get over.

But Hogni answered, "Nay, let no man hinder her from dying; for no gain will she be to us, nor has she been gainsome since she came hither!"

Now she bade bring forth much gold, and bade all those come thither who would have wealth: then she caught up a sword, and thrust it under her armpit, and sank aside upon the pillows, and said, "Come, take gold whoso will!"

But all held their peace, and she said, "Take the gold, and be glad thereof!"

And therewith she spake unto Gunnar, "Now for a little while will I tell of that which shall come to pass hereafter; for speedily shall ye be at one again with Gudrun by the rede of Grimhild the Wise-wife; and the daughter of Gudrun and Sigurd shall be called Swanhild, the fairest of all women born. Gudrun shall be given to Atli, yet not with her good will. Thou shalt be fain to get Oddrun, but that shall Atli forbid thee; but privily shall ye meet, and much shall she love thee. Atli shall bewray thee, and cast thee into a worm-close, and thereafter shall Atli and his sons be slain, and Gudrun shall be their slayer; and afterwards shall the great waves bear her to the burg of King Jonakr, to whom she shall bear sons of great fame: Swanhild shall be sent from the land and given to King Jormunrek; and her shall bite the rede of Bikki, and therewithal is the kin of you clean gone; and more sorrows therewith for Gudrun.

"And now I pray thee, Gunnar, one last boon.—Let make a great bale on the plain meads for all of us; for me and for Sigurd, and for those who were slain with him, and let that be covered over with cloth dyed red by the folk of the Gauls, and burn me thereon on one side of the King of the Huns, and on the other those men of mine, two at the head and two at the feet, and two hawks withal; and even so is all shared equally; and lay there betwixt us a drawn sword, as in the other days when we twain stepped into one bed together; and then may we have the name of man and wife, nor shall the door swing to at the heel of him as I go behind him. Nor shall that be a niggard company if there follow him those five bond-women and eight bondmen, whom my father gave me, and those burn there withal who were slain with Sigurd.

"Now more yet would I say, but for my wounds, but my life-breath flits; the wounds open,—yet have I said sooth."

Now is the dead corpse of Sigurd arrayed in olden wise, and a mighty bale is raised, and when it was somewhat kindled, there was laid thereon the dead corpse of Sigurd Fafnir's-bane, and his son of three winters whom Brynhild had let slay, and Guttorm withal; and when the bale was all ablaze, thereunto was Brynhild borne out, when she had spoken with her bower-maidens, and bid them take the gold that she would give; and then died Brynhild, and was burned there by the side of Sigurd, and thus their life-days ended.

Chapter 33

Gudrun wedded to Atli

Now so it is, that whoso heareth these tidings sayeth, that no such an one as was Sigurd was left behind him in the world, nor ever was such a man brought forth because of all the worth of him, nor may his name ever minish by eld in the Dutch Tongue nor in all the Northern Lands, while the world standeth fast.

The story tells that, on a day, as Gudrun sat in her bower, she fell to saying, "Better was life in those days when I had Sigurd; he who was far above other men as gold is above iron, or the leek over other grass of the field, or the hart over other wild things; until my brethren begrudged me such a man, the first and best of all men; and so they might not sleep or they had slain him. Huge clamour made Grani when he saw his master and lord sore wounded, and then I spoke to him even as with a man, but he fell drooping down to the earth, for he knew that Sigurd was slain."

Thereafter Gudrun gat her gone into the wild woods, and heard on all ways round about her the howling of wolves, and deemed death a merrier thing than life. Then she went till she came to the hall of King Alf, and sat there in Denmark with Thora, the daughter of Hakon, for seven seasons, and abode with good welcome. And she set forth her needlework before her, and did thereinto many deeds and great, and fair plays after the fashion of those days, swords and byrnies, and all

the gear of kings, and the ship of King Sigmund sailing along
the land; yea, and they wrought there, how they fought, Sigar
and Siggeir, south in Fion. Such was their disport; and now
Gudrun was somewhat solaced of her grief.

So Grimhild comes to hear where Gudrun has take up her
abode, and she calls her sons to talk with her, and asks
whether they will make atonement to Gudrun for her son and
her husband, and said that it was but meet and right to do so.

Then Gunnar spake, and said that he would atone for her
sorrows with gold.

So they send for their friends, and array their horses, their
helms, and their shields, and their byrnies, and all their war-
gear; and their journey was furnished forth in the noblest
wise, and no champion who was of the great men might abide
at home; and their horses were clad in mail-coats, and every
knight of them had his helm done over with gold or with
silver.

Grimhild was of their company, for she said that their
errand would never be brought fairly to pass if she sat at
home.

There were well five hundred men, and noble men rode
with them. There was Waldemar of Denmark, and Eymod and
Jarisleif withal. So they went into the hall of King Alf, and
there abode them the Longbeards, and Franks, and Saxons:
they fared with all their war-gear, and had over them red
fur-coats. Even as the song says—

> Byrnies short cut,
> Strong helms hammered,
> Girt with good swords,
> Red hair gleaming.

They were fain to choose good gifts for their sister, and
spake softly to her, but in none of them would she trow. Then
Gunnar brought unto her a drink mingled with hurtful things,
and this she must needs drink, and with the drinking thereof
she had no more memory of their guilt against her.

But in that drink was blended the might of the earth and the
sea with the blood of her son; and in that horn were all letters
cut and reddened with blood, as is said hereunder—

On the horn's face were there
All the kin of letters
Cut aright and reddened,
How should I rede them rightly?
The ling-fish long
Or the land of Hadding,
Wheat-ears unshorn,
And wild things' inwards.

In that beer were mingled
Many ills together,
Blood of all the wood
And brown-burnt acorns,
The black dew of the hearth,
The God-doomed dead beast's inwards,
And the swine's liver sodden
Because all wrongs that deadens.

And so now, when their hearts are brought anigh to each other, great cheer they made: then came Grimhild to Gudrun, and spake—

"All hail to thee, daughter! I give thee gold and all kinds of good things to take to thee after thy father, dear-bought rings and bed-gear of the maids of the Huns, the most courteous and well dight of all women; and thus is thy husband atoned for: and thereafter shalt thou be given to Atli, the mighty king, and be mistress of all his might. Cast not all thy friends aside for one man's sake, but do according to our bidding."

Gudrun answers, "Never will I wed Atli the King: unseemly it is for us to get offspring betwixt us."

Grimhild says, "Nourish not thy wrath; it shall be to thee as if Sigurd and Sigmund were alive when thou hast borne sons."

Gudrun says, "I cannot take my heart from thoughts of him, for he was the first of all men."

Grimhild says, "So it is shapen that thou must have this king and none else."

Says Gudrun, "Give not this man to me, for an evil thing shall came upon thy kin from him, and to his own sons shall he deal evil, and be rewarded with a grim revenge thereafter."

Then waxed Grimhild fell at those words, and spake, "Do even as we bid thee, and take therefore great honour, and our friendship, and the steads withal called Vinbjorg and Valbjorg."

And such might was in the words of her, that even so must it come to pass.

Then Gudrun spake, "Thus then must it needs befall, howsoever against the will of me, and for little joy shall it be and for great grief."

Then men leaped on their horses, and their women were set in wains. So they fared four days a-riding and other four a-shipboard, and yet four more again by land and road, till at the last they came to a certain high-built hall; then came to meet Gudrun many folk thronging; and an exceedingly goodly feast was there made, even as the word had gone between either kin, and it passed forth in most proud and stately wise. And at that feast drinks Atli his bridal with Gudrun; but never did her heart laugh on him, and little sweet and kind was their life together.

Chapter 34

Atli bids the Giukings to him

NOW TELLS the tale that on a night King Atli woke from sleep and spake to Gudrun—

"Medreamed," said he, "that thou didst thrust me through with a sword."

Then Gudrun areded the dream, and said that it betokened fire, whenas folk dreamed of iron. "It befalls of thy pride belike, in that thou deemest thyself the first of men."

Atli said, "Moreover I dreamed that here waxed two sorb-tree saplings, and fain I was that they should have no scathe of me; then these were riven up by the roots and reddened with blood, and borne to the bench, and I was bidden eat thereof.

"Yea, yet again I dreamed that two hawks flew from my hand hungry and unfed, and fared to hell, and meseemed their hearts were mingled with honey, and that I ate thereof.

"And then again I dreamed that two fair whelps lay before me yelling aloud, and that the flesh of them I ate, though my will went not with the eating."

Gudrun says, "Nowise good are these dreams, yet shall they come to pass; surely thy sons are nigh to death, and many heavy things shall fall upon us."

"Yet again I dreamed," said he, "and methought I lay in a bath, and folk took counsel to slay me."

Now these things wear away with time, but in nowise was their life together fond.

Now falls Atli to thinking of where may be gotten that plenteous gold which Sigurd had owned, but King Gunnar and his brethren were lords thereof now.

Atli was a great king and mighty, wise, and a lord of many men; and now he falls to counsel with his folk as to the ways of them. He wotted well that Gunnar and his brethren had more wealth than any others might have; and so he falls to the rede of sending men to them, and bidding them to a great feast, and honouring them in diverse wise, and the chief of those messengers was hight Vingi.

Now the queen wots of their conspiring, and misdoubts her that this would mean some beguiling of her brethren: so she cut runes, and took a gold ring, and knit therein a wolf's hair, and gave it into the hands of the king's messengers.

Thereafter they go their ways according to the king's bidding; and or ever they came aland Vingi beheld the runes, and turned them about in such a wise as if Gudrun prayed her brethren in her runes to go meet King Atli.

Thereafter they came to the hall of King Gunnar, and had good welcome at his hands, and great fires were made for them, and in great joyance they drank of the best of drink.

Then spake Vingi, "King Atli sends me hither, and is fain that ye go to his house and home in all glory, and take of him exceeding honours, helms and shields, swords and byrnies, gold and goodly raiment, horses, hosts of war, and great and wide lands, for, saith he, he is fainest of all things to bestow his realm and lordship upon you."

Then Gunnar turned his head aside, and spoke to Hogni—

"In what wise shall we take this bidding? might and wealth he bids us take; but no kings know I who have so much gold as we have, whereas we have all the hoard which lay once on Gnitaheath; and great are our chambers, and full of gold, and weapons for smiting, and all kinds of raiment of war, and well I wot that amidst all men my horse is the best, and my sword the sharpest, and my gold the most glorious."

Hogni answers, "A marvel is it to me of his bidding, for seldom hath he done in such a wise, and ill-counselled will it be to wend to him; lo now, when I saw those dear-bought things the king sends us I wondered to behold a wolf's hair knit to a certain gold ring; belike Gudrun deems him to be minded as a wolf towards us, and will have naught of our faring."

But withal Vingi shows him the runes which he said Gudrun had sent.

Now the most of folk go to bed, but these drank on still with certain others; and Kostbera, the wife of Hogni, the fairest of women, came to them, and looked on the runes.

But the wife of Gunnar was Glaumvor, a great-hearted wife.

So these twain poured out, and the kings drank, and were exceeding drunken, and Vingi notes it, and says—

"Naught may I hide that King Atli is heavy of foot and over-old for the warding of his realm; but his sons are young and of no account: now will he give you rule over his realms while they are yet thus young, and most fain will he be that he have the joy thereof before all others."

Now so it befell both that Gunnar was drunk, and that great dominion was held out to him, nor might he work against the fate shapen for him; so he gave his word to go, and tells Hogni his brother thereof.

But he answered, "Thy word given must even stand now, nor will I fail to follow thee, but most loth am I to this journey."

Chapter 35

The Dreams of the Wives of the Giukings

So WHEN men had drunk their fill, they fared to sleep; then falls Kostbera to beholding the runes, and spelling over the letters, and sees that beneath were other things cut, and that the runes are guileful; yet because of her wisdom she had skill to read them aright. So then she goes to bed by her husband; but when they awoke, she spake unto Hogni—

"Thou art minded to wend away from home—ill-counselled is that; abide till another time! Scarce a keen reader of runes art thou, if thou deemest thou hast beheld in them the bidding of thy sister to this journey: lo, I read the runes, and had marvel of so wise a woman as Gudrun is, that she should have miscut them; but that which lieth underneath beareth your bane with it,—yea, either she lacked a letter, or others have dealt guilefully with the runes.

"And now hearken to my dream; for therein methought there fell in upon us here a river exceeding strong, and brake up the timbers of the hall."

He answered, "Full oft are ye evil of mind, ye women, but for me, I was not made in such wise as to meet men with evil who deserve no evil; belike he will give us good welcome."

She answered, "Well, the thing must ye yourselves prove, but no friendship follows this bidding:—but yet again I dreamed that another river fell in here with a great and grimly

211

rush, and tore up the dais of the hall, and brake the legs of both you brethren; surely that betokeneth somewhat."

He answers, "Meadows along our way, whereas thou didst dream of the river; for when we go through the meadows, plentifully doth the seeds of the hay hang about our legs."

"Again I dreamed," she says, "that thy cloak was afire, and that the flame blazed up above the hall."

Says he, "Well, I wot what that shall betoken; here lieth my fair-dyed raiment, and it shall burn and blaze, whereas thou dreamedst of the cloak."

"Methought a bear came in," she says, "and brake up the king's high-seat, and shook his paws in such a wise that we were all adrad thereat, and he gat us all together into the mouth of him, so that we might avail us naught, and thereof fell great horror on us."

He answered, "Some great storm will befall, whereas thou hadst a white bear in thy mind."

"An erne methought came in," she says, "and swept adown the hall, and drenched me and all of us with blood, and ill shall that betoken, for methought it was the double of King Atli."

He answered, "Full oft do we slaughter beasts freely, and smite down great neat for our cheer, and the dream of the erne has but to do with oxen; yea, Atli is heart-whole toward us."

And therewithal they cease this talk.

Chapter 36

Of the Journey of the Giukings to King Atli

Now TELLS the tale of Gunnar, that in the same wise it fared with him; for when they awoke, Glaumvor his wife told him many dreams which seemed to her like to betoken guile coming; but Gunnar areded them all in other wise.

"This was one of them," said she; "methought a bloody sword was borne into the hall here, wherewith thou wert thrust through, and at either end of that sword wolves howled."

The king answered, "Cur dogs shall bite me belike; blood-stained weapons oft betoken dogs' snappings."

She said, "Yet again I dreamed—that women came in, heavy and drooping, and chose thee for their mate; may-happen these would be thy fateful women."

He answered, "Hard to arede is this, and none may set aside the fated measure of his days, nor it is unlike that my time is short."

So in the morning they arose, and were minded for the journey, but some letted them herein.

Then cried Gunnar to the man who is called Fjornir—

"Arise, and give us to drink goodly wine from great tuns, because mayhappen this shall be very last of all our feasts; for belike if we die the old wolf shall come by the gold, and that bear shall nowise spare the bite of his war-tusks."

Then all the folk of his household brought them on their way weeping.

The son of Hogni said—

"Fare ye well with merry tide."

The more part of their folk were left behind; Solar and

213

Gnœvar, the sons of Hogni, fared with them, and a certain great champion, named Orkning, who was the brother of Kostbera.

So folk followed them down to the ships, and all letted them of their journey, but attained to naught therein.

Then spake Glaumvor, and said—

"O Vingi, most like that great ill hap will come of thy coming, and mighty and evil things shall betide in thy travelling."

He answered, "Hearken to my answer; that I lie not aught: and may the high gallows and all things of grame have me, if I lie one word!"

Then cried Kostbera, "Fare ye well with merry days."

And Hogni answered, "Be glad of heart, howsoever it may fare with us!"

And therewith they parted, each to their own fate. Then away they rowed, so hard and fast, that well-nigh the half of the keel slipped away from the ship, and so hard they laid on to the oars that thole and gunwale brake.

But when they came aland they made their ship fast, and then they rode awhile on their noble steeds through the murk wild-wood.

And now they behold the king's army, and huge uproar, and the clatter of weapons they hear from thence; and they see there a mighty host of men, and the manifold array of them, even as they wrought there: and all the gates of the burg were full of men.

So they rode up to the burg, and the gates thereof were shut; then Hogni brake open the gates, and therewith they ride into the burg.

Then spake Vingi, "Well might ye have left this deed undone; go to now, bide ye here while I go seek your gallows-tree! Softly and sweetly I bade you hither, but an evil thing abode thereunder; short while to bide ere ye are tied up to that same tree!"

Hogni answered, "None the more shall we waver for that cause; for little methinks have we shrunk aback whenas men fell to fight; and naught shall it avail thee to make us afeard,— and for an ill fate hast thou wrought."

And therewith they cast him down to earth, and smote him with their axe-hammers till he died.

Chapter 37

The Battle in the Burg of King Atli

THEN THEY rode unto the king's hall, and King Atli arrayed his host for battle, and the ranks were so set forth that a certain wall there was betwixt them and the brethren.

"Welcome hither," said he. "Deliver unto me that plenteous gold which is mine of right; even the wealth which Sigurd once owned, and which is now Gudrun's of right."

Gunnar answered, "Never gettest thou that wealth; and men of might must thou meet here, or ever we lay by life if thou wilt deal with us in battle; ah, belike thou settest forth this feast like a great man, and wouldst not hold thine hand from erne and wolf!"

"Long ago I had it in my mind," said Atli, "to take the lives of you, and be lord of the gold, and reward you for that deed of shame, wherein ye beguiled the best of all your affinity; but now shall I revenge him."

Hogni answered, "Little will it avail to lie long brooding over that rede, leaving the work undone."

And therewith they fell to hard fighting, at the first brunt with shot.

But therewithal came the tidings to Gudrun, and when she heard thereof she grew exceeding wroth, and cast her mantle from her, and ran out and greeted those new-comers, and kissed her brethren, and showed them all love,—and the last of all greetings was that betwixt them.

Then said she, "I thought I had set forth counsels whereby ye should not come hither, but none may deal with his shapen fate." And withal she said, "Will it avail aught to seek for peace?"

But stoutly and grimly they said nay thereto. So she sees that the game goeth sorely against her brethren, and she gathers to her great stoutness of heart, and does on her a mail-coat and takes to her a sword, and fight by her brethren, and goes as far forward as the bravest of manfolk: and all spoke in one wise that never saw any fairer defence than in her.

Now the men fell thick, and far before all others was the fighting of those brethren, and the battle endured a long while unto midday; Gunnar and Hogni went right through the folk of Atli, and so tells the tale that all the mead ran red with blood; the sons of Hogni withal set on stoutly.

Then spake Atli the king, "A fair host and a great have we, and mighty champions withal, and yet have many of us fallen, and but evil am I apaid in that nineteen of my champions are slain, and but six left alive."

And therewithal was there a lull in the battle.

Then spake Atli the king, "Four brethren were we, and now am I left alone; great affinity I gat to me, and deemed my fortune well sped thereby; a wife I had, fair and wise, high of mind, and great of heart; but no joyance may I have of her wisdom, for little peace is betwixt us,—but ye—ye have slain many of my kin, and beguiled me of realm and riches, and for the greatest of all woes have slain my sister withal."

Quoth Hogni, "Why babblest thou thus? thou wert the first to break the peace. Thou didst take my kinswoman and pine her to death by hunger, and didst murder her, and take her wealth; an ugly deed for a king!—meet for mocking and laughter I deem it, that thou must needs make long tale of thy woes; rather will I give thanks to the Gods that thou fallest into ill."

Chapter 38

Of the Slaying of the Giukings

Now KING ATLI eggs on his folk to set on fiercely, and eagerly they fight; but the Guikings fell on so hard that King Atli gave back into the hall, and within doors was the fight, and fierce beyond all fights.

That battle was the death of many a man, but such was the ending thereof, that there fell all the folk of those brethren, and they twain alone stood up on their feet, and yet many more must fare to hell first before their weapons.

And now they fell on Gunnar the king, and because of the host of men that set on him was hand laid on him, and he was cast into fetters; afterwards fought Hogni, with the stoutest heart and the greatest manlihood; and he felled to earth twenty of the stoutest of the champions of King Atli, and many he thrust into the fire that burnt amidst the hall, and all were of one accord that such a man might scarce be seen; yet in the end was he borne down by many and taken.

Then said King Atli, "A marvellous thing how many men have gone their ways before him! Cut the heart from out of him, and let that be his bane!"

Hogni said, "Do according to thy will; merrily will I abide whatso thou wilt do against me; and thou shalt see that my heart is not adrad, for hard matters have I made trial of ere now, and all things that may try a man was I fain to bear, whiles yet I was unhurt; but now sorely am I hurt, and thou alone henceforth will bear mastery in our dealings together."

Then spake a counsellor of King Atli, "Better rede I see thereto; take we the thrall Hjalli, and give respite to Hogni; for this thrall is made to die, since the longer he lives the less worth shall he be."

The thrall hearkened, and cried out aloft, and fled away anywhither where he might hope for shelter, crying out that a hard portion was his because of their strife and wild doings, and an ill day for him whereon he must be dragged to death from his sweet life and his swine-keeping. But they caught him, and turned a knife against him, and he yelled and screamed or ever he felt the point thereof.

Then in such wise spake Hogni as a man seldom speaketh who is fallen into hard need, for he prayed for the thrall's life, and said that these shrieks he could not away with, and that it were a lesser matter to him to play out the play to the end; and therewithal the thrall gat his life as for that time: but Gunnar and Hogni are both laid in fetters.

Then spake King Atli with Gunnar the king, and bade him tell out concerning the gold, and where it was, if he would have his life.

But he answered, "Nay, first will I behold the bloody heart of Hogni, my brother."

So now they caught hold of the thrall again, and cut the heart from out of him, and bore it unto King Gunnar, but he said—

"The faint heart of Hjalli may ye here behold, little like the proud heart of Hogni, for as much as it trembleth now, more by the half it trembled whenas it lay in the breast of him."

So now they fell on Hogni even as Atli urged them, and cut the heart from out of him, but such was the might of his manhood, that he laughed while he abode that torment, and all wondered at his worth, and in perpetual memory is it held sithence.

Then they showed it to Gunnar, and he said—

"The mighty heart of Hogni, little like the faint heart of Hjalli, for little as it trembleth now, less it trembled whenas in his breast it lay! But now, O Atli, even as we die so shalt thou die; and lo, I alone wot where the gold is, nor shall Hogni be to tell thereof now; to and fro played the matter in my mind whiles we both lived, but now have I myself determined for myself, and the Rhine river shall rule over the gold, rather than that the Huns shall bear it on the hands of them."

Then said King Atli, "Have away the bondsman;" and so they did.

But Gudrun called to her men, and came to Atli, and said—

"May it fare ill with thee now and from henceforth, even as thou hast ill held to thy word with me!"

So Gunnar was cast into a worm-close, and many worms abode him there, and his hands were fast bound; but Gudrun sent him a harp, and in such wise did he set forth his craft, that wisely he smote the harp, smiting it with his toes, and so excellently well he played, that few deemed they had heard such playing, even when the hand had done it. And with such might and power he played, that all the worms fell asleep in the end, save one adder only, great and evil of aspect, that crept unto him and thrust its sting into him until it smote his heart; and in such wise with great hardihood he ended his life days.

Chapter 39

The End of Atli and his Kin and Folk

NOW THOUGHT Atli the King that he had gained a mighty victory, and spake to Gudrun even as mocking her greatly, or as making himself great before her. "Gudrun," saith he, "thus hast thou lost thy brethren, and thy very self hast brought it about."

She answers, "In good liking livest thou, whereas thou thrustest these slayings before me, but mayhappen thou wilt rue it, when thou hast tried what is to come hereafter; and of all I have, the longest-lived matter shall be the memory of thy cruel heart, nor shall it go well with thee whiles I live."

He answered and said, "Let there be peace betwixt us; I will atone for thy brethren with gold and dear-bought things, even as thy heart may wish."

She answers, "Hard for a long while have I been in our dealings together, and now I say, that while Hogni was yet alive thou mightest have brought it to pass; but now mayest thou never atone for my brethren in my heart; yet oft must we women be overborne by the might of you men; and now are all my kindred dead and gone, and thou alone art left to rule over me: wherefore now this is my counsel that we make a great feast, wherein I will hold the funeral of my brother and of thy kindred withal."

In such wise did she make herself soft and kind in words, though far other things forsooth lay thereunder, but he hearkened to her gladly, and trusted in her words, whereas she made herself sweet of speech.

So Gudrun held the funeral feast for her brethren, and King Atli for his men, and exceeding proud and great was this feast.

But Gudrun forgat not her woe, but brooded over it, how she might work some mighty shame against the king; and at nightfall she took to her the sons of King Atli and her as they played about the floor; the younglings waxed heavy of cheer, and asked what she would with them.

"Ask me not," she said; "ye shall die, the twain of you!"

Then they answered, "Thou mayest do with thy children even as thou wilt, nor shall any hinder thee, but shame there is to thee in the doing of this deed."

Yet for all that she cut the throats of them.

Then the king asked where his sons were, and Gudrun answered, "I will tell thee, and gladden thine heart by the telling; lo now, thou didst make a great woe spring up for me in the slaying of my brethren; now hearken and hear my rede and my deed; thou hast lost thy sons, and their heads are become beakers on the board here, and thou thyself hast drunken the blood of them blended with wine; and their hearts I took and roasted them on a spit, and thou hast eaten thereof."

King Atli answered, "Grim art thou in that thou hast murdered thy sons, and given me their flesh to eat, and little space passes betwixt ill deed of thine and ill deed."

Gudrun said, "My heart is set on the doing to thee of as great shame as may be; never shall the measure of ill be full to such a king as thou art."

The king said, "Worser deeds hast thou done than men have to tell of, and great unwisdom is there in such fearful redes; most meet art thou to be burned on bale when thou hast first been smitten to death with stones, for in such wise wouldst thou have what thou hast gone a weary way to seek."

She answered, "Thine own death thou foretellest, but another death is fated for me."

And many other words they spake in their wrath.

Now Hogni had a son left alive, hight Niblung, and great wrath of heart he bare against King Atli; and he did Gudrun to wit that he would avenge his father. And she took his words

well, and they fell to counsel together thereover, and she said
it would be great goodhap if it might be brought about.

So on a night, when the king had drunken, she gat him to
bed, and when he was laid asleep, thither to him came Gudrun
and the son of Hogni.

Gudrun took a sword and thrust it through the breast of
King Atli, and they both of them set their hands to the deed,
both she and the son of Hogni.

Then Atli the king awoke with the wound, and cried out,
"No need of binding or salving here!—who art thou who hast
done the deed?"

Gudrun says, "Somewhat have I, Gudrun, wrought therein,
and somewhat withal the son of Hogni."

Atli said, "Ill it beseemed to thee to do this, though somewhat of wrong was between us; for thou wert wedded to me
by the rede of thy kin, and dower paid I for thee; yea, thirty
goodly knights, and seemly maidens, and many men besides;
and yet wert thou not content, but if thou shouldst rule over
the lands King Budli owned: and thy mother-in-law full oft
thou lettest sit a-weeping."

Gudrun said, "Many false words hast thou spoken, and of
naught I account them; oft, indeed, was I fell of mood, but
much didst thou add thereto. Full oft in this thy house did
frays befall, and kin fought kin, and friend fought friend, and
made themselves big one against the other; better days had I
whenas I abode with Sigurd, when we slew kings, and took
their wealth to us, but gave peace to whomso would, and the
great men laid themselves under our hands, and might we gave
to him of them who would have it; then I lost him, and a little
thing was it that I should bear a widow's name, but the greatest of griefs that I should come to thee—I who had aforetime
the noblest of all kings, while for thee, thou never barest out
of the battle aught but the worser lot."

King Atli answered, "Naught true are thy words, nor will
this our speech better the lot of either of us, for all is fallen
now to naught; but now do to me in seemly wise, and array
my dead corpse in noble fashion."

"Yea, that will I," she says, "and let make for thee a goodly grave, and build for thee a worthy abiding place of stone, and wrap thee in fair linen, and care for all that needful is."

So therewithal he died, and she did according to her word: and then they cast fire into the hall.

And when the folk and men of estate awoke amid that dread and trouble, naught would they abide the fire, but smote each the other down, and died in such wise; so there Atli the king, and all his folk, ended their life-days. But Gudrun had no will to live longer after this deed so wrought, but nevertheless her ending day was not yet come upon her.

Now the Volsungs and the Giukings, as folk tell in tale, have been the greatest-hearted and the mightiest of all men, as ye may well behold written in the songs of old time.

But now with the tidings just told were these troubles stayed.

Chapter 40

How Gudrun cast herself into the Sea, but was brought ashore again

GUDRUN HAD a daughter by Sigurd hight Swanhild; she was the fairest of all women, eager-eyed as her father, so that few durst look under the brows of her; and as far did she excel other woman-kind as the sun excels the other lights of heaven.

But on a day went Gudrun down to the sea, and caught up stones in her arms, and went out into the sea, for she had will to end her life. But mighty billows drave her forth along the sea, and by means of their upholding was she borne along till she came at the last to the burg of King Jonakr, a mighty king, and lord of many folk. And he took Gudrun to wife, and their children were Hamdir, and Sorli and Erp; and there was Swanhild nourished withal.

Chapter 41

Of the Wedding and Slaying of Swanhild

JORMUNREK WAS the name of a mighty king of those days, and his son was called Randver. Now this king called his son to talk with him, and said, "Thou shalt fare on an errand of mine to King Jonakr, with my counsellor Bikki, for with King Jonakr is nourished Swanhild, the daughter of Sigurd Fafnir's-bane; and I know for sure that she is the fairest may dwelling under the sun of this world; her above all others would I have to my wife, and thou shalt go woo her for me."

Randver answered, "Meet and right, fair lord, that I should go on thine errands."

So the king set forth this journey in seemly wise, and they fare till they come to King Jonakr's abode, and behold Swanhild, and have many thoughts concerning the treasure of her goodliness.

But on a day Randver called the king to talk with him, and said, "Jormunrek the King would fain be thy brother-in-law, for he has heard tell of Swanhild, and his desire it is to have her to wife, nor may it be shown that she may be given to any mightier man then he is one."

The King says, "This is an alliance of great honour, for a man of fame he is."

Gudrun says, "A wavering trust, the trust in luck that it change not!"

Yet because of the king's furthering, and all the matters that went herewith, is the wooing accomplished; and Swanhild went to the ship with a goodly company, and sat in the stern beside the king's son.

Then spake Bikki to Randver, "How good and right it were if thou thyself had to wife so lovely a woman rather than the old man there."

Good seemed that word to the heart of the king's son, and he spake to her with sweet words, and she to him in likewise.

So they came aland and go unto the king, and Bikki said unto him, "Meet and right it is, lord, that thou shouldst know what is befallen, though hard it be to tell of, for the tale must be concerning thy beguiling, whereas thy son has gotten to him the full love of Swanhild, nor is she other than his harlot; but thou, let not the deed be unavenged."

Now many an ill rede had he given the king or this, but of all his ill redes did this sting home the most; and still would the king hearken to all his evil redes; wherefore he, who might nowise still the wrath within him, cried out that Randver should be taken and tied up to the gallows-tree.

And as he was led to the gallows he took his hawk and plucked the feathers from off it, and bade show it to his father; and when the king saw it, then he said, "Now may folk behold that he deemeth my honour to be gone away from me, even as the feathers of this hawk;" and therewith he bade deliver him from the gallows.

But in that while had Bikki wrought his will, and Randver was dead-slain.

And, moreover, Bikki spake, "Against none hast thou more wrongs to avenge thee of than against Swanhild; let her die a shameful death."

"Yea," said the king, "we will do after thy counsel."

So she was bound in the gate of the burg, and horses were driven at her to tread her down; but when she opened her eyes wide, then the horses durst not trample her; so when Bikki beheld that, he bade draw a bag over the head of her; and they did so, and therewith she lost her life.

Chapter 42

Gudrun sends her Sons to avenge Swanhild

Now GUDRUN heard of the slaying of Swanhild, and spake to her sons, "Why sit ye here in peace amid merry words, whereas Jormunrek hath slain your sister, and trodden her under foot of horses in shameful wise? No heart ye have in you like to Gunnar or Hogni; verily they would have avenged their kinswoman!"

Hamdir answered, "Little didst thou praise Gunnar and Hogni, whereas they slew Sigurd, and thou wert reddened in the blood of him, and ill were thy brethren avenged by the slaying of thine own sons: yet not so ill a deed were it for us to slay King Jormunrek, and so hard thou pushest us on to this that we may naught abide thy hard words."

Gudrun went about laughing now, and gave them to drink from mighty beakers, and thereafter she got for them great byrnies and good, and all other weed of war.

Then spake Hamdir, "Lo now, this is our last parting, for thou shalt hear tidings of us, and drink one grave-ale over us and over Swanhild."

So therewith they went their ways.

But Gudrun went unto her bower, with heart swollen with sorrow, and spake—

"To three men was I wedded, and first to Sigurd Fafnir's-bane, and he was bewrayed and slain, and of all griefs was that the greatest grief. Then was I given to King Atli, and so fell was my heart toward him that I slew in the fury of my grief his children and mine. Then gave I myself to the sea, but the billows thereof cast me out aland, and to this king then was I given; then gave I Swanhild away out of the land with mighty wealth; and lo my next greatest sorrow after Sigurd, for under horses' feet was she trodden and slain; but the grimmest and ugliest of woes was the casting of Gunnar into the Worm-close, and the hardest was the cutting of Hogni's heart from him.

"Ah, better would it be if Sigurd came to meet me, and I went my ways with him, for here bideth now behind with me neither son nor daughter to comfort me. Oh, mindest thou not, Sigurd, the words we spoke when we went into one bed together, that thou wouldst come and look on me; yea, even from thine abiding place among the dead?"

And thus had the words of her sorrow an end.

Chapter 43

The Latter End of all the Kin of the Giukings

Now TELLETH the tale concerning the sons of Gudrun, that she had arrayed their war-raiment in such wise, that no steel would bite thereon; and she bade them play not wtih stones or other heavy matters, for that it would be to their scathe if they did so.

And now, as they went on their way, they met Erp, their brother, and asked him in what wise he would help them.

He answered, "Even as hand helps hand, or foot helps foot."

But that they deemed naught at all, and slew him there and then. Then they went their ways, nor was it long or ever Hamdir stumbled, and thrust down his hand to steady himself, and spake therewith—

"Naught but a true thing spake Erp, for now should I have fallen, had not hand been to steady me."

A little after Sorli stumbled, but turned about on his feet, and so stood, and spake—

"Yea now had I fallen, but that I steadied myself with both feet."

And they said they had done evilly with Erp their brother.

But on they fare till they come to the abode of King Jormunrek, and they went up to him and set on him forthwith, and Hamdir cut both hands from him and Sorli both feet. Then spake Hamdir—

"Off were the head if Erp were alive; our brother, whom we slew on the way, and found out our deed too late." Even as the Song says,—

> Off were the head
> If Erp were alive yet,
> Our brother the bold,
> Whom we slew by the way,
> The well-famed in warfare.

Now in this must they turn away from the words of their mother, whereas they had to deal with stones. For now men fell on them, and they defended themselves in good and manly wise, and were the scathe of many a man, nor would iron bite on them.

But there came thereto a certain man, old of aspect and one-eyed, and he spake—

"No wise men are ye, whereas ye cannot bring these men to their end."

Then the king said, "Give us rede thereto, if thou canst."

He said, "Smite them to the death with stones."

In such wise was it done, for the stones flew thick and fast from every side, and that was the end of their life-days.

And now has come to an end the whole root and stem of the Giukings.

> Now may all earls
> Be bettered in mind,
> May the grief of all maidens
> Ever be minished,
> For this tale of trouble
> So told to its ending.

Certain Songs

from

The Elder Edda,

Which Deal with the Story of the Volsungs

Part of the Second Lay of Helgi Hundings-bane

HELGI WEDDED Sigrun, and they begat sons together, but Helgi lived not to be old; for Dag, the son of Hogni, sacrificed to Odin, praying that he might avenge his father. So Odin lent Dag his spear, and Dag met Helgi, his brother-in-law, at a place called Fetter-grove, and thrust him through with that spear, and there fell Helgi dead; but Dag rode to Sevafell, and told Sigrun of the news.

> Loth am I, sister,
> Of sorrow to tell thee,
> For by hard need driven
> Have I drawn on thee greeting;
> This morning fell
> In Fetter-grove
> The king well deemed
> The best in the wide world,
> Yea, he who stood
> On the necks of the strong.

Sigrun.

> All oaths once sworn
> Shall bite thee sore,
> The oaths that to Helgi
> Once thou swarest
> At the bright white
> Water of Lightening,
> And at the cold rock
> That the sea runneth over.

May the ship sweep not on
That should sweep at its swiftest,
Though the wind desired
Behind thee driveth!
May the horse never run
That should run at his most might
When from thy foe's face
Thou hast most need to flee!

May the sword never bite
That thou drawest from scabbard,
But and if round thine head
In wrath it singeth!

Then should meet price be paid
For Helgi's slaying
When a wolf thou wert
Out in the wild-wood,
Empty of good things,
Empty of gladness,
With no meat for thy mouth
But dead men's corpses!

Dag.

With mad words thou ravest,
Thy wits are gone from thee,
When thou for thy brother
Such ill fate biddest;
Odin alone
Let all this bale loose,
Casting the strife-runes
'Twixt friends and kindred.

Rings of red gold
Will thy brother give thee,
And the stead of Vandil
And the lands of Vigdale;
Have half of the land
For thy sorrow's healing,

O ring-arrayed sweetling
For thee and thy sons!

Sigrun.

No more sit I happy
At Sevafell;
At day-dawn, at night
Naught love I my life
Till broad o'er the people
My lord's light breaketh;
Till his war-horse runneth
Beneath him hither,
Well wont to the gold bit—
Till my king I welcome.

In such wise did Helgi
Deal fear around
To all his foes
And all their friends
As when the goat runneth
Before the wolf's rage
Filled with mad fear
Down from the fell.

As high above all lords
Did Helgi bear him
As the ash-tree's glory
From the thorn ariseth,
Or as the fawn
With the dew-fall sprinkled
Is far above
All other wild things,
As his horns go gleaming
'Gainst the very heavens.

A barrow was raised above Helgi, but when he came to Valhall, then Odin bade him be lord of all things there, even as he; so Helgi sang—

> Now shalt thou, Hunding,
> For the help of each man
> Get ready the foot-bath,
> And kindle the fire;
> The hounds shalt thou bind
> And give heed to the horses,
> Give wash to the swine
> Ere to sleep thou goest.

A bondmaid of Sigrun went in the evening-tide by Helgi's mound, and there she saw how Helgi rode toward it with a great company; then she sang—

> It is vain things' beguiling
> That methinks I behold,
> Or the ending of all things,
> As ye ride, O ye dead men,
> Smiting with spurs
> Your horses' sides?
> Or may dead warriors
> Wend their ways homeward?

The Dead.

> No vain things' beguiling
> Is that thou beholdest,
> Nor the ruin of all things;
> Though thou lookest upon us,
> Though we smite with spurs
> Our horses' sides;
> Rather dead warriors
> May wend their ways homeward.

Then went the bondmaid home, and told Sigrun, and and sang—

> Go out, Sigrun
> From Sevafell,

If thou listest to look on
The lord of thy people!
For the mound is uncovered
Thither is Helgi come,
And his wounds are bleeding,
But the king thee biddeth
To come and stay
That stream of sorrow.

So Sigrun went into the mound to Helgi, and sang—

Now am I as fain
Of this fair meeting,
As are the hungry
Hawks of Odin,
When they wot of the slaying
Of the yet warm quarry,
Or bright with dew
See the day a-dawning.

Ah, I will kiss
My king laid lifeless,
Ere thou castest by
Thy blood-stained byrny.
O Helgi, thy hair
Is thick with death's rime,
With the dew of the dead
Is my love all dripping;
Dead-cold are the hands
Of the son of Hogni!
How for thee, O my king,
May I win healing?

Helgi.

Thou alone, Sigrun
Of Sevafell,
Hast so done that Helgi
With grief's dew drippeth;

O clad in gold
Cruel tears thou weepest,
Bright May of the Southlands,
Or ever thou sleepest:
Each tear in blood falleth
On the breast of thy lord,
Cold-wet and bitter-sharp
Swollen with sorrow.

Ah, we shall drink
Dear draughts and lovely,
Though we have lost
Both life and lands;
Neither shall any
Sing song of sorrow,
Though in my breast
Be wounds wide to behold:
For now are brides
In the mound abiding;
Kings' daughters sit
By us departed.

Now Sigrun arrayed a bed in the mound, and sang:

Here, Helgi, for thee
A bed have I dight,
Kind without woe,
O kin of the Ylfings!
To thy bosom, O king,
Will I come and sleep soft,
As I was wont
When my lord was living.

Helgi.

Now will I call
Naught not to be hoped for
Early or late
At Sevafell,

When thou in the arms
Of a dead man art laid,
White maiden of Hogni,
Here in the mound:
And thou yet quick,
O King's daughter!

Now needs must I ride
On the reddening ways;
My pale horse must tread
The highway aloft:
West must I go
To Windhelm's bridge
Ere the war-winning crowd
Hall-crower waketh.

So Helgi rode his ways: and the others gat them gone home
to the house. But the next night Sigrun bade the bondwoman
have heed of the mound. So at nightfall, whenas Sigrun came
to the mound, she sang:

Here now would he come,
If to come he were minded;
Sigmund's offspring
From the halls of Odin.
O me the hope waneth
Of Helgi's coming;
For high on the ash-boughs
Are the ernes abiding,
And all folk drift
Toward the Thing of the dreamland.

The Bondmaid.

Be not foolish of heart,
And fare all alone
To the house of the dead,
O Hero's daughter!
For more strong and dreadful

> In the night season
> Are all dead warriors
> Than in the daylight.

But a little while lived Sigrun, because of her sorrow and trouble. But in old time folk trowed that men should be born again, though their troth be now deemed but an old wife's doting. And so, as folk say, Helgi and Sigrun were born again, and at that tide was he called Helgi the Scathe of Hadding, and she Kara the daughter of Halfdan; and she was a Valkyria, even as is said in the Lay of Kara.

Part of the Lay of Sigrdrifa

Now this is my first counsel,
That thou with thy kin
Be guiltless, guileless ever,
Nor hasty of wrath,
Despite of wrong done—
Unto the dead good that doeth.

Lo the second counsel,
That oath thou swearest never,
But trusty oath and true:
Grim tormenting
Gripes troth-breakers;
Cursed wretch is the wolf of vows.

This is my third rede,
That thou at the Thing
Deal not with the fools of folk;
For unwise man
From mouth lets fall
Worser word than well he wotteth.

Yet hard it is
That holding of peace
When men shall deem thee dastard,
Or deem the lie said soothly;
But woeful is home-witness,

Unless right good thou gettest it
  Ah, on another day
  Drive the life from out him,
And pay the liar back for his lying.

  Now behold the fourth rede:
  If ill witch thee bideth,
Woe-begetting by the way,
  Good going further
  Rather than guesting,
Though thick night be on thee.

  Far-seeing eyes
  Need all sons of men
Who wend in wrath to war;
  For baleful women
  Bide oft by the highway,
Swords and hearts to soften.

  And now the fifth rede:
  As fair as thou seest
Brides on the bench abiding,
  Let not love's silver
  Rule over thy sleeping;
Draw no woman to kind kissing!

  For the sixth thing, I rede
  When men sit a-drinking
Amid ale-words and ill-words,
  Deal thou naught
  With the drunken fight-stayes,
For wine stealeth wit from many.

  Brawling and drink
  Have brought unto men
Sorrow sore oft enow;
  Yea, bane unto some,
  And to some weary bale;
Many are the griefs of mankind.

For the seventh, I rede thee,
If strife thou raisest
With a man right high of heart,
Better fight a-field
Than burn in the fire
Within thine hall fair to behold.

The eighth rede that I give thee:
Unto all ill look thou,
And hold thine heart from all beguiling;
Draw to thee no maiden,
No man's wife bewray thou,
Urge them not unto unmeet pleasure.

This is the ninth counsel:
That thou have heed of dead folk
Whereso thou findest them a-field;
Be they sick-dead,
Be they sea-dead,
Or come to ending by war-weapons.

Let bath be made
For such men fordone,
Wash thou hands and feet thereof,
Comb their hair and dry them
Ere the coffin has them;
Then bid them sleep full sweetly.

This for the tenth counsel:
That thou give trust never
Unto oaths of foeman's kin,
Be'st thou bane of his brother,
Or hast thou felled his father;
Wolf in young son waxes,
Though he with gold be gladdened.

For wrong and hatred
Shall rest them never,
Nay, nor sore sorrow.

Both wit and weapons
Well must the king have
Who is fain to be the foremost.

The last rede and eleventh:
Until all ill look thou,
And watch thy friends' ways ever.
Scarce durst I look
For long life for thee, king:
Strong trouble ariseth now already.

The Lay called the Short Lay of Sigurd

SIGURD of yore,
Sought the dwelling of Giuki,
As he fared, the young Volsung,
After fight won;
Troth he took
From the two brethren;
Oath swore they betwixt them,
Those bold ones of deed.

A may they gave to him
And wealth manifold,
Gudrun the young,
Giuki's daughter:
They drank and gave doom
Many days together,
Sigurd the young,
And the sons of Giuki.

Until they wended
For Brynhild's wooing,
Sigurd a-riding
Amidst their rout;
The wise young Volsung
Who knew of all ways—
Ah! he had wed her,
Had fate so willed it.

Southlander Sigurd
A naked sword,
Bright, well grinded,
Laid betwixt them;
No kiss he won
From the fair woman,
Nor in arms of his
Did the Hun King hold her,
Since he gat the young maid
For the son of Giuki.

No lack in her life
She wotted of now,
And at her death-day
No dreadful thing
For a shame indeed
Or a shame in seeming;
But about and betwixt
Went baleful fate.

Alone, abroad,
She sat of an evening,
Of full many things
She fell a-talking:
"O for my Sigurd!
I shall have death,
Or my fair, my lovely,
Laid in mine arms.

"For the word once spoken,
I sorrow sorely—
His queen is Gudrun,
I am wed to Gunnar;
The dread Norns wrought for us
A long while of woe."

Oft with heart deep
In dreadful thoughts,
O'er ice-fields and ice-hills
She fared a-night time,

When he and Gudrun
Were gone to their fair bed,
And Sigurd wrapped
The bed-gear round her.

"Ah! now the Hun King
His queen in arms holdeth,
While love I go lacking,
And all things longed for
With no delight
But in dreadful thought."

These dreadful things
Thrust her toward murder:
—"Listen, Gunnar,
For thou shalt lose
My wide lands,
Yea, me myself!
Never love I my life,
With thee for my lord—

"I will fare back thither
From whence I came,
To my nighest kin
And those that know me
There shall I sit
Sleeping my life away,
Unless thou slayest
Sigurd the Hun King,
Making thy might more
E'en than his might was!

"Yea, let the son fare
After the father,
And no young wolf
A long while nourish!
For on each man lieth
Vengeance lighter,
And peace shall be surer
If the son live not."

Adrad was Gunnar,
Heavy-hearted was he,
And in doubtful mood
Day-long he sat.
For naught he wotted,
Nor might see clearly
What was the seemliest
Of deeds to set hand to;

What of all deeds
Was best to be done:
For he minded the vows
Sworn to the Volsung,
And the sore wrong
To be wrought against Sigurd.

Wavered his mind
A weary while,
No wont it was
Of those days worn by,
That queens should flee
From the realms of their kings.

"Brynhild to me
Is better than all,
The child of Budli
Is the best of women.
Yea, and my life
Will I lay down,
Ere I am twinned
From that woman's treasure."

He bade call Hogni
To the place where he bided;
With all the trust that might be,
Trowed he in him.

"Wilt thou bewray Sigurd
For his wealth's sake?

Good it is to rule
O'er the Rhine's metal;
And well content
Great wealth to wield,
Biding in peace
And blissful days."

One thing alone Hogni
Had for an answer:
"Such doings for us
Are naught seemly to do;
To rend with sword
Oaths once sworn,
Oaths once sworn,
And troth once plighted.

"Nor know we on mould,
Men of happier days,
The while we four
Rule over the folk;
While the bold in battle,
The Hun King, bides living.

"And no nobler kin
Shall be known afield,
If our five sons
We long may foster;
Yea, a goodly stem
Shall surely wax.
—But I clearly see
In what wise it standeth,
Brynhild's sore urging
O'ermuch on thee beareth.

"Guttorm shall we
Get for the slaying,
Our younger brother
Bare of wisdom;
For he was out of

All the oaths sworn,
All the oaths sworn,
And the plighted troth."

Easy to rouse him
Who of naught recketh!
—Deep stood the sword
In the heart of Sigurd.

There, in the hall,
Gat the high-hearted vengeance;
For he cast his sword
At the reckless slayer:
Out at Guttorm
Flew Gram the mighty,
The gleaming steel
From Sigurd's hand.

Down fell the slayer
Smitten asunder;
The heavy head
And the hands fell one way,
But the feet and such like
Aback where they stood.

Gudrun was sleeping
Soft in the bed,
Empty of sorrow
By the side of Sigurd:
When she awoke
With all pleasure gone,
Swimming in blood
Of Frey's beloved.

So sore her hands
She smote together,
That the great-hearted
Gat raised in bed;
—"O Gudrun, weep not

So woefully,
Sweet lovely bride,
For thy brethren live for thee!

"A young child have I
For heritor;
Too young to win forth
From the house of his foes.—

Black deeds and ill
Have they been a-doing,
Evil rede
Have they wrought at last.

"Late, late, rideth with them
Unto the Thing,
Such sister's son,
Though seven thou bear,—
—But well I wot
Which way all goeth;
Alone wrought Brynhild
This bale against us.

"That maiden loved me
Far before all men,
Yet wrong to Gunnar
I never wrought;
Brotherhood I heeeded
And all bounden oaths,
That none should deem me
His queen's darling."

Weary sighed Gudrun,
As the king gat ending,
And so sore her hands
She smote together,
That the cups arow
Rang out therewith,
And the geese cried on high
That were in the homefield.

Then laughed Brynhild,
Budli's daughter,
Once, once only,
From out her heart;
When to her bed
Was borne the sound
Of the sore greeting
Of Giuki's daughter.

Then, quoth Gunnar,
The king, the hawk-bearer,
"Whereas, thou laughest,
O hateful woman,
Glad on thy bed,
No good it betokeneth:
Why lackest thou else
Thy lovely hue?
Feeder of foul deeds,
Fey do I deem thee,

"Well worthy art thou
Before all women,
That thine eyes should see
Atli slain of us;
That thy brother's wounds
Thou shouldst see a-bleeding,
That his bloody hurts
Thine hands should bind."

"No man blameth thee, Gunnar,
Thou hast fulfilled death's measure
But naught Atli feareth
All thine ill will;
Life shall he lay down
Later than ye,
And still bear more might
Aloft than thy might.

"I shall tell thee, Gunnar,
Though well the tale thou knowest,
In what early days

Ye dealt abroad your wrong:
Young was I then,
Worn with no woe,
Good wealth I had
In the house of my brother!

"No mind had I
That a man should have me,
Or ever ye Giukings,
Rode into our garth;
There ye sat on your steeds
Three kings of the people—
—Ah! that that faring
Had never befallen!

"Then spake Atli
To me apart,
And said that no wealth
He would give unto me,
Neither gold nor lands
If I would not be wedded;
Nay, and no part
Of the wealth apportioned,
Which in my first days
He gave me duly;
Which in my first days
He counted down.

"Wavered the mind
Within me then,
If to fight I should fall
And the felling of folk,
Bold in byrny
Because of my brother;
A deed of fame
Had that been to all folk,
But to many a man
Sorrow of mind.

"So I let all sink
Into peace at the last:

More grew I minded
For the mighty treasure,
The red-shining rings
Of Sigmund's son;
For no man's wealth else
Would I take unto me.

"For myself had I given
To that great king
Who sat amid gold
On the back of Grani;

Nought were his eyen
Like to your eyen,
Nor in any wise
Went his visage with yours;
Though ye might deem you
Due kings of men.

"One I loved,
One, and none other,
The gold-decked may
Had no doubtful mind;
Thereof shall Atli
Wot full surely,
When he getteth to know
I am gone to the dead.

"Far be it from me,
Feeble and wavering,
Ever to love
Another's love—
—Yet shall my woe
Be well avenged."

Up rose Gunnar,
The great men's leader,
And cast his arms
About the queen's neck
And all went nigh

One after other,
With their whole hearts
Her heart to turn.

But then all these
From her neck she thrust,
Of her long journey
No man should let her.

Then called he Hogni
To have talk with him:
"Let all folk go
Forth into the hall,
Thine with mine—
—O need sore and mighty!—
To wot if we yet
My wife's parting may stay.
Till the time's wearing
Some hindrance wax."

One answer Hogni
Had for all;
"Nay, let hard need
Have rule thereover,
And no man let her
Of her long journey!
Never born again,
May she come back thence!

"Luckless she came
To the lap of her mother,
Born into the world
For utter woe,
To many a man
For heart-whole mourning."

Upraised he turned
From the talk and the trouble,
To where the gem-field
Dealt out goodly treasure;

As she looked and beheld
All the wealth that she had,
And the hungry bondmaids,
And maids of the hall.

With no good in her heart
She donned her gold byrny,
Ere she thrust the sword-point
Through the midst of her body:
On the bolster's far side
Sank she adown,
And, smitten with sword,
Still bethought her of redes.

"Let all come forth
Who are fain the red gold,
Or things less worthy
To win from my hands;
To each one I give
A necklace gilt over,
Wrought hangings and bed-gear
And bright woven weed."

All they kept silence,
And thought what to speak,
Then all at once
Answer gave:
"Full enow are death-doomed,
Fain are we to live yet,
Maids of the hall
All meet work winning."

From her wise heart at last
The linen-clad damsel,
The one of few years
Gave forth the word:
"I will that none driven
By hand or by word,
For our sake should lose
Well-loved life.

"Thou on the bones of you
Surely shall burn,
Less dear treasure
At your departing
Nor with Menia's Meal
Shall ye come to see me."

"Sit thee down, Gunnar,
A word must I say to thee
Of the life's ruin
Of thy lightsome bride—
—Nor shall thy ship
Swim soft and sweetly
For all that I
Lay life adown.

"Sooner than ye might deem
Shall ye make peace with Gudrun,
For the wise woman
Shall lull in the young wife
The hard memory
Of her dead husband.

"There is a may born
Reared by her mother,
Whiter and brighter
Than is the bright day;
She shall be Swanhild,
She shall be Sunbeam.

"Thou shalt give Gudrun
Unto a great one,
Noble, well-praised
Of the world's folk;
Not with her goodwill,
Or love shalt thou give her;
Yet will Atli
Come to win her,
My very brother,
Born of Budli.

—"Ah! many a memory
Of how ye dealt with me,
How sorely, how evilly
Ye ever beguiled me,
How all pleasure left me
The while my life lasted!—

"Fain wilt thou be
Oddrun to win,
But thy good liking
Shall Atli let;
But in secret wise
Shall ye win together,
And she shall love thee
As I had loved thee,
If in such wise
Fate had willed it.

"But with all ill
Shall Atli sting thee,
Into the strait worm-close
Shall he cast thee.

"But no long space
Shall slip away
Ere Atli too
All life shall lose.
Yea, all his weal
With the life of his sons,
For a dreadful bed
Dights Gudrun for him,
From a heart sore laden,
With the sword's sharp edge.

"More seemly for Gudrun,
Your very sister,
In death to wend after
Her love first wed;
Had but good rede
To her been given,

Or if her heart
Had been like to my heart.

—"Faint my speech groweth—
But for our sake
Ne'er shall she lose
Her life beloved;
The sea shall have her,
High billows bear her
Forth unto Jonakr's
Fair land of his fathers.

"There shall she bear sons,
Stays of a heritage,
Stays of a heritage,
Jonakr's sons;
And Swanhild shall she
Send from the land,
That may born of her,
The may born of Sigurd.

"Her shall bite
The rede of Bikki,
Whereas for no good
Wins Jormunrek life;
And so is clean perished
All the kin of Sigurd,
Yea, and more greeting,
And more for Gudrun.

"And now one prayer
Yet pray I of thee—
The last word of mine
Here in the world—
So broad on the field
Be the burg of the dead
That fair space may be left
For us all to lie down,
All those that died
At Sigurd's death!

"Hang round that burg
Fair hangings and shields,
Web by Gauls woven,
And folk of the Gauls:
There burn the Hun King
Lying beside me.

"But on the other side
Burn by the Hun King
Those who served me
Strewn with treasure;
Two at the head,
And two at the feet,
Two hounds therewith,
And two hawks moreover:
Then is all dealt
With even dealing.

"Lay there amidst us
The ring-dight metal,
The sharp-edged steel,
That so lay erst;
When we both together
Into one bed went,
And were called by the name
Of man and wife.

"Never, then, belike
Shall clash behind him
Valhall's bright door
With rings bedight:
And if my fellowship
Followeth after,
In no wretched wise
Then shall we wend.

"For him shall follow
My five bondmaids,
My eight bondsmen,
No borel folk:

Yea, and my fosterer,
And my father's dower
That Budli of old days
Gave to his dear child.

"Much have I spoken,
More would I speak,
If the sword would give me
Space for speech;
But my words are waning,
My wounds are swelling—
Naught but truth have I told—
—And now make I ending."

The Hell-Ride of Brynhild

AFTER THE death of Brynhild were made two bales, one for Sigurd, and that was first burned; but Brynhild was burned on the other, and she was in a chariot hung about with goodly hangings.

And so folk say that Brynhild drave in her chariot down along the way to Hell, and passed by an abode where dwelt a certain giantess, and the giantess spake:—

> "Nay, with my goodwill
> Never goest thou
> Through this stone-pillared
> Stead of mine!
> More seemly for thee
> To sit sewing the cloth,
> Than to go look on
> The love of another.

> "What dost thou, going
> From the land of the Gauls,
> O restless head,
> To this mine house?
> Golden girl, hast thou not,
> If thou listest to hearken,
> In sweet wise from thy hands
> The blood of men washen?"

Brynhild.

"Nay, blame me naught,
Bride of the rock-hall,
Though I roved a warring
In the days that were;
The higher of us twain
Shall I ever be holden
When of our kind
Men make account."

The Giant-woman.

"Thou, O Brynhild,
Budli's daughter,
Wert the worst ever born
Into the world:
For Giuki's children
Death hast thou gotten,
And turned to destruction
Their goodly dwelling."

Brynhild.

"I shall tell thee
True tale from my chariot,
O thou who naught wottest,
If thou listest to wot;
How for me they have gotten
Those heirs of Giuki,
A loveless life,
A life of lies.

"Hild under helm,
The Hlymdale people,
E'en those who knew me,
Ever would call me.

"The changeful shapes
Of us eight sisters,
The wise king bade

Under oak-tree to bear:
Of twelve winters was I,
If thou listest to wot,
When I sware to the young lord
Oaths of love.

"Thereafter gat I
Mid the folk of the Goths,
For Helmgunnar the old,
Swift journey to Hell,
And gave to Aud's brother
The young, gain and glory;
Whereof overwrath
Waxed Odin with me.

"So he shut me in shield-wall
In Skata grove,
Red shields and white
Close set around me;
And bade him alone
My slumber to break
Who in no land
Knew how to fear.

"He set round my hall,
Toward the south quarter,
The Bane of all trees
Burning aloft;
And ruled that he only
Thereover should ride
Who should bring me the gold
O'er which Fafnir brooded.

"Then upon Grani rode
The goodly gold-strewer
To where my fosterer
Ruled his fair dwelling.
He who alone there
Was deemed best of all,

The War-lord of the Danes,
Well worthy of men.

"In peace did we sleep
Soft in one bed,
As though he had been
Naught but my brother:
There as we lay
Through eight nights wearing,
No hand in love
On each other we laid.

"Yet thence blamed me, Gudrun,
Giuki's daughter,
That I had slept
In the arms of Sigurd;
And then I wotted
As I fain had not wotted,
That they had bewrayed me
In my betrothals.

"Ah! for unrest
All too long
Are men and women
Made alive!
Yet we twain together
Shall wear through the ages,
Sigurd and I.—
—Sink adown, O giant-wife!"

Fragments of the Lay of Brynhild

Hogni said.

What hath wrought Sigurd
Of any wrong-doing
That the life of the famed one
Thou art fain of taking?

Gunnar said.

To me has Sigurd
Sworn many oaths,
Sworn many oaths,
And sworn them lying,
And he bewrayed me
When it behoved him
Of all folk to his troth
To be the most trusty.

Hogni said.

Thee hath Brynhild
Unto all bale,
And all hate whetted,
And a work of sorrow;
For she grudges to Gudrun
All goodly life;
And to thee the bliss
Of her very body.

. . . . .

Some of the wolf roasted,
Some minced the worm,
Some unto Guttorm
Gave the wolf-meat,
Or ever they might
In their lust for murder
On the high king
Lay deadly hand.

Sigurd lay slain
On the south of the Rhine.
High from the fair tree
Croaked forth the raven,
"Ah, yet shall Atli
On you redden edges,
The old oaths shall weigh
On your souls, O warriors."

Without stood Gudrun,
Giuki's daughter,
And the first word she said
Was even this word:
"Where then is Sigurd,
Lord of the Warfolk,
Since my kin
Come riding the foremost?"

One word Hogni
Had for an answer:
"Our swords have smitten
Sigurd asunder,
And the grey horse hangs drooping
O'er his lord lying dead."

Then quoth Brynhild,
Budli's daughter;
"Good weal shall ye have
Of weapons and lands,
That Sigurd alone
Would surely have ruled

If he had lived
But a little longer.

"Ah, nothing seemly
For Sigurd to rule
Giuki's house
And the folk of the Goths,
When of him five sons
For the slaying of men,
Eager for battle
Should have been begotten!"

Then laughed Brynhild—
Loud rang the whole house—
One laugh only
From out her heart:
"Long shall your bliss be
Of lands and people,
Whereas the famed lord
You have felled to the earth!"

Then spake Gudrun,
Giuki's daughter;
"Much thou speakest,
Many things fearful,
All grame be on Gunnar
The bane of Sigurd!
From a heart full of hate
Shall come heavy vengeance."

Forth sped the even
Enow there was drunken,
Full enow was there
Of all soft speech;
And all men got sleep
When to bed they were gotten;
Gunnar only lay waking
Long after all men.

His feet fell he to moving,
Fell to speak to himself

The waster of men,
Still turned in his mind
What on the bough
Those twain would be saying,
The raven and erne
As they rode their ways homeward.

But Brynhild awoke,
Budli's daughter,
May of the shield-folk,
A little ere morning:
"Thrust ye on, hold ye back,
—Now all harm is wrought,—
To tell of my sorrow,
Or to let all slip by me?"

All kept silence
After her speaking,
None might know
That woman's mind,
Or why she must weep
To tell of the work
That laughing once
Of men she prayed.

Brynhild spake.

In dreams, O Gunnar,
Grim things fell on me;
Dead-cold the hall was,
And my bed was a-cold,
And thou, lord, wert riding
Reft of all bliss,
Laden with fetters
'Mid the host of thy foemen.

So now all ye,
O House of the Niblungs,
Shall be brought to naught,
O ye oath-breakers!

Think'st thou not, Gunnar,
How that betid,
When ye let the blood run
Both in one footstep?
With ill reward
Hast thou rewarded
His heart so fain
To be the foremost!

As well was seen
When he rode his ways,
That king of all worth,
Unto my wooing;
How the host-destroyer
Held to the vows
Sworn beforetime,
Sworn to the young king.

For his wounding-wand
All wrought with gold,
The king beloved
Laid between us;
Without were its edges
Wrought with fire,
But with venom-drops
Deep dyed within.

Thus this song telleth of the death of Sigurd, and setteth
forth how that they slew him without doors; but some say
that they slew him within doors, sleeping in his bed. But the
Dutch Folk say that they slew him out in the wood: and so
sayeth the ancient song of Gudrun, that Sigurd and the sons
of Giuki were riding to the Thing whenas he was slain. But
all with one accord say that they bewrayed him in their troth
with him, and fell on him as he lay unarrayed and unawares.

The Second or Ancient Lay of Gudrun

THIODREK THE King was in Atli's house, and had lost there the more part of his men: so there Thiodrek and Gudrun bewailed their troubles one to the other, and she spake and said:—

> A may of all mays
> My mother reared me
> Bright in bower;
> Well loved I my brethren,
> Until that Giuki
> With gold arrayed me,
> With gold arrayed me,
> And gave me to Sigurd.

> Such was my Sigurd,
> Among the sons of Giuki
> As is the green leek
> O'er the low grass waxen,
> Or a hart high-limbed
> Over hurrying deer,
> Or glede-red gold
> Over grey sliver.

> Till me they begrudged,
> Those my brethren,
> The fate to have him,
> Who was first of all men;

Nor might they sleep,
Nor sit a-dooming,
Ere they let slay
My well-loved Sigurd.

Grani ran to the Thing,
There was clatter to hear,
But never came Sigurd
Himself thereunto;
All the saddle-girt beasts
With blood were besprinkled,
As faint with the way
Neath the slayers they went.

Then greeting I went
With Grani to talk,
And with tear-furrowed cheeks
I bade him tell all;
But drooping laid Grani,
His head in the grass,
For the steed well wotted
Of his master's slaying.

A long while I wandered,
Long my mind wavered,
Ere the kings I might ask
Concerning my king.

Then Gunnar hung head,
But Hogni told
Of the cruel slaying
Of my Sigurd:
"On the water's far side
Lies, smitten to death,
The bane of Guttorm
To the wolves given over.

"Go, look on Sigurd,
On the ways that go southward,
There shalt thou hear

The ernes high screaming,
The ravens a-croaking
As their meat they crave for;
Thou shalt hear the wolves howling
Over thine husband."

"How hast thou, Hogni,
The heart to tell me,
Me of joy made empty,
Of such misery?
Thy wretched heart
May the ravens tear
Wide over the world,
With no men mayst thou wend."

One thing Hogni
Had for answer,
Fallen from his high heart,
Full of all trouble:
"More greeting yet,
O Gudrun, for thee,
If my heart the ravens
Should rend asunder!"

Thence I turned
From the talk and the trouble
To go a leasing
What the wolves had left me;
No sigh I made
No smote hands together,
Nor did I wail
As other women
When I sat over
My Sigurd slain.

Night methought it,
And the moonless dark,
When I sat in sorrow
Over Sigurd:
Better than all things

I deemed it would be
If they would let me
Cast my life by,
Or burn me up
As they burn the birch-wood.

From the fell I wandered
Five days together,
Until the high hall
Of Half lay before me;
Seven seasons there
I sat with Thora,
The daughter of Hacon,
Up in Denmark.

My heart to gladden
With gold she wrought
Southland halls
And swans of the Dane-folk;
There had we painted
The chiefs a-playing;
Fair our hands wrought
Folk of the kings.

Red shields we did,
Doughty knights of the Huns,
Hosts spear-dight, hosts helm-dight,
All a high king's fellows;
And the ships of Sigmund
From the land swift sailing;
Heads gilt over
And prows fair graven.

On the cloth we broidered
That tide of their battling,
Siggeir and Siggar,
South in Fion.

Then heard Grimhild,
The Queen of Gothland,

How I was abiding,
Weighed down with woe;
And she thrust the cloth from her
And called to her sons,
And oft and eagerly
Asked them thereof,
Who for her son
Would their sister atone,
Who for her lord slain
Would lay down weregild.

Fain was Gunnar
Gold to lay down
All wrongs to atone for,
And Hogni in likewise;
Then she asked who was fain
Of faring straightly,
The steed to saddle
To set forth the wain,
The horse to back,
And the hawk to fly,
To shoot forth the arrow
From out the yew-bow.

Valdarr the Dane-king
Came with Jarisleif
Eymod the third went
Then went Jarizskar;

In kingly wise
In they wended,
The host of the Longbeards;
Red cloaks had they,
Byrnies short-cut,
Helms strong hammered,
Girt with glaives,
And hair red-gleaming.

Each would give me
Gifts desired,

Gifts desired,
Speech dear to my heart,
If they might yet,
Despite my sorrow,
Win back my trust,
But in them nought I trusted.

Then brought me Grimhild
A beaker to drink of,
Cold and bitter,
Wrong's memory to quench;
Made great was that drink
With the might of the earth,
With the death-cold sea
And the blood that Son holdeth.

On that horn's face were there
All the kin of letters
Cut aright and reddened,
How should I rede them rightly
The ling-fish long
Of the land of Hadding,
Wheat-ears unshorn,
And wild things' inwards.

In that mead were mingled
Many ills together,
Blood of all the wood,
And brown-burnt acorns;
The black dew of the hearth,
And god-doomed dead beasts' inwards,
And the swine's liver sodden,
For wrongs late done that deadens.

Then waned my memory
When that was within me,
Of my lord 'mid the hall
By the iron laid low.
Three kings came
Before my knees

Ere she herself
Fell to speech with me.

"I will give to thee, Gudrun,
Gold to be glad with,
All the great wealth
Of thy father gone from us,
Rings of red gold
And the great hall of Lodver,
And all fair hangings left
By the king late fallen.

"Maids of the Huns
Woven pictures to make,
And work fair in gold
Till thou deem'st thyself glad.
Alone shalt thou rule
O'er the riches of Budli,
Shalt be made great with gold,
And be given to Atli."

"Never will I
Wend to a husband,
Or wed the brother
Of Queen Brynhild;
Naught it beseems me
With the son of Budli
Kin to bring forth,
Or to live and be merry."

"Nay, the high chiefs
Reward not with hatred,
For take heed that I
Was the first in this tale!
To thy heart shall it be
As if both these had life,
Sigurd and Sigmund,
When thou hast borne sons."

"Naught may I, Grimhild,
Seek after gladness,

Nor deem aught hopeful
Of any high warrior,
Since wolf and raven
Were friends together,
The greedy, the cruel,
O'er great Sigurd's heart-blood."

"Of all men that can be
For the noblest of kin
This king have I found,
And the foremost of all;
Him shalt thou have
Till with eld thou art heavy—
Be thou ever unwed,
If thou wilt naught of him!"

"Nay, nay, bid me not
With thy words long abiding
To take unto me
That balefullest kin;
This king shall bid Gunnar
Be stung to his bane,
And shall cut the heart
From out of Hogni.

"Nor shall I leave life
Ere the keen lord,
The eager in sword-play,
My hand shall make end of."

Grimhild a-weeping
Took up the word then,
When the sore bale she wotted
Awaiting her sons,
And the bane hanging over
Her offspring beloved.

"I will give thee, moreover,
Great lands, many men,
Wineberg and Valberg,

If thou wilt but have them;
Hold them lifelong,
And live happy, O daughter!"

"Then him must I take
From among kingly men,
'Gainst my heart's desire,
From the hands of my kinsfolk;
But no joy I look
To have from that lord:
Scarce may my brother's bane
Be a shield to my sons."

Soon was each warrior
Seen on his horse,
But the Gaulish women
Into wains were gotten;
Then seven days long
O'er a cold land we rode,
And for seven other
Clove we the sea-waves.
But with the third seven
O'er dry land we wended.

There the gate-wardens
Of the burg, high and wide,
Unlocked the barriers
Ere the burg-garth we rode to.—

. . . . . .
. . . . . .

Atli woke me
When meseemed I was
Full evil of heart
For my kin dead slain.

"In such wise did the Norns
Wake me or now."—
Fain was he to know
Of this ill foreshowing—

"That methought, O Gudrun,
Giuki's daughter,
That thou setst in my heart
A sword wrought for guile."

"For fires tokening I deem it
That dreaming of iron,
But for pride and for lust
The wrath of fair women
Against some bale
Belike, I shall burn thee
For thy solace and healing
Though hateful thou art."

"In the fair garth methought
Had saplings fallen
E'en such as I would
Should have waxen ever;
Uprooted were these,
And reddened with blood,
And borne to the bench,
And folk bade me eat of them.

"Methought from my hand then
Went hawks a-flying
Lacking their meat
To the land of all ill;
Methought that their hearts
Mingled with honey,
Swollen with blood
I ate amid sorrow.
"Lo, next two whelps
From my hands I loosened,
Joyless were both,
And both a-howling;
And now their flesh
Became naught but corpses,
Whereof must I eat
But sore against my will."

"O'er the prey of the fishers
Will folk give doom;
From the bright white fish
The heads will they take;
Within a few nights,
Fey as they are,
A little ere day
Of that draught will they eat."

Ne'er since lay I down,
Ne'er since would I sleep,
Hard of heart, in my bed:—
That deed have I to do.

The Song of Atli

GUDRUN, GIUKI's daughter, avenged her brethren, as is told far and wide: first she slew the sons of Atli, and then Atli himself; and she burned the hall thereafter, and all the household with it: and about these matters is this song made:—

> In days long gone
> Sent Atli to Gunnar
> A crafty one riding,
> Knefrud men called him;
> To Giuki's garth came he,
> To the hall of Gunnar,
> To the benches gay-dight,
> And the gladsome drinking.
>
> There drank the great folk
> 'Mid the guileful one's silence,
> Drank wine in their fair hall:
> The Huns' wrath they feared,
> When Knefrud cried
> In his cold voice.
> As he sat on the high seat,
> That man of the Southland:
>
> "Atli has sent me
> Riding swift on his errands
> On the bit-griping steed

Through dark woodways unbeaten,
To bid thee, King Gunnar,
Come to his fair bench
With helm well-adorned,
To the home of King Atli.

"Shields shall ye have there
And spears ashen-shafted,
Helms ruddy with gold,
And hosts of the Huns;
Saddle-gear silver-gilt,
Shirts red as blood,
The hedge of the warwife,
And horses bit-griping.

"And he saith he will give you
Gnitaheath widespread,
And whistling spears
And prows well-gilded,
Mighty wealth
With the stead of Danpi,
And that noble wood
Men name the Murkwood."

Then Gunnar turned head
And spake unto Hogni:
"What rede from thee, high one,
Since such things we hear?
No gold know I
On Gnitaheath,
That we for our parts
Have not portion as great.

"Seven halls we have
Fulfilled of swords,
And hilts of gold
Each sword there has;
My horse is the best,
My blade is the keenest;
Fair my bow o'er the bench is,

Gleams my byrny with gold;
Brightest helm, brightest shield,
From Kiar's dwelling ere brought—
Better all things I have
Then all things of the Huns."

Hogni said.

"What mind has our sister
That a ring she hath sent us
In weed of wolves clad?
Bids she not to be wary?
For a wolf's hair I found
The fair ring wreathed about;
Wolf beset shall the way be
If we wend on this errand."

No sons whetted Gunnar,
Nor none of his kin,
Nor learned men nor wise men,
Nor such as were mighty.
Then spake Gunnar
E'en as a king should speak,
Glorious in mead-hall
From great heart and high:

"Rise up now, Fiornir,
Forth down the benches
Let the gold-cups of great ones
Pass in hands of my good-men!
Well shall we drink wine,
Draughts dear to our hearts,
Though the last of all feasts
In our fair house this be!

"For the wolves shall rule
O'er the wealth of the Niblungs,
With the pine-woods' wardens
If Gunnar perish:
And the black-felled bears

With fierce teeth shall bite
For the glee of the dog-kind,
If again comes not Gunnar."

Then good men never shamed,
Greeting aloud,
Led the great king of men
From the garth of his home;
And cried the fair son
Of Hogni the king:
"Fare happy, O Lords,
Whereso your hearts lead you!"

Then the bold knights
Let their bit-griping steeds
Wend swift o'er the fells,
Tread the murk-wood unknown,
All the Hunwood was shaking
As the hardy ones fared there;
O'er the green meads they urged
Their steeds shy of the goad.

Then Atli's land saw they;
Great towers and strong,
And the bold men of Bikki,
Aloft on the burg:
The Southland folks' hall
Set with benches about,
Dight with bucklers well bounden,
And bright white shining shields.

There drank Atli,
The awful Hun king,
Wine in his fair hall;
Without were the warders,
Gunnar's folk to have heed of,
Lest they had fared thither
With the whistling spear
War to wake 'gainst the king.

But first came their sister
As they came to the hall,
Both her brethren she met,
With beer little gladdened:
"Bewrayed art thou, Gunnar!
What dost thou great king
To deal war to the Huns?
Go thou swift from the hall!

"Better, brother, hadst thou
Fared here in thy byrny
Than with helm gaily dight
Looked on Atli's great house:
Thou hadst sat then in saddle
Through days bright with the sun
Fight to awaken
And fair fields to redden:

"O'er the folk fate makes pale
Should the Norn's tears have fallen,
The shield-mays of the Huns
Should have known of all sorrow;
And King Atli himself
To worm-close should be brought;
But now is the worm-close
Kept but for thee."

Then spake Gunnar
Great 'mid the people:
"Over-late sister
The Niblungs to summon;
A long way to seek
The helping of warriors,
The high lords unshamed,
From the hills of the Rhine!"

·   ·   ·   ·   ·

·   ·   ·   ·   ·

Seven Hogni beat down
With his sword sharp-grinded,

And the eighth man he thrust
Amidst of the fire.
Ever so shall famed warrior
Fight with his foemen,
As Hogni fought
For the hand of Gunnar.

But on Gunnar they fell,
And set him in fetters,
And bound hard and fast
That friend of Burgundians;
Then the warrior they asked
If he would buy life,
Buy life with gold
That king of the Goths.

Nobly spake Gunnar,
Great lord of the Niblungs;
"Hogni's bleeding heart first
Shall lie in mine hand,
Cut from the breast
Of the bold-riding lord,
With bitter-sharp knife
From the son of the king."

With guile the great one
Would they beguile,
On the wailing thrall
Laid they hand unwares,
And cut the heart
From out of Hjalli,
Laid it bleeding on trencher
And bare it to Gunnar.

"Here have I the heart
Of Hjalli the trembler,
Little like the heart
Of Hogni the hardy:
As much as it trembleth
Laid on the trencher,

By the half more it trembled
In the breast of him hidden."

Then laughed Hogni
When they cut the heart from him,
From the crest-smith yet quick,
Little thought he to quail.
The hard acorn of thought
From the high king they took,
Laid it bleeding on trencher
And bare it Gunnar.

"Here have I the heart
Of Hogni the hardy,
Little like to the heart
Of Hjalli the trembler.
Howso little it quaketh
Laid here on the dish,
Yet far less it quaked
In the breast of him laid.

"So far mayst thou bide
From men's eyen, O Atli,
As from that treasure
Thou shalt abide!

"Beholden in my heart
Is hidden for ever
That hoard of the Niblungs,
Now Hogni is dead.
Doubt threw me two ways
While the twain of us lived,
But all that is gone
Now I live on alone.

"The great Rhine shall rule
O'er the hate-raising treasure,
That gold of the Niblungs,
The seed of the gods:
In the weltering water

Shall that wealth lie a-gleaming,
Or it shine on the hands
Of the children of Huns!"

Then cried Atli,
King of the Hun-folk,
"Drive forth your wains now
The slave is fast bounden."
And straightly thence
The bit-shaking steeds
Drew the hoard-warden,
The war-god to his death.

Atli the great king,
Rode upon Glaum,
With shields set round about,
And sharp thorns of battle:
Gudrun, bound by wedlock
To these, victory made gods of,
Held back her tears
As the hall she ran into.

"Let it fare with thee, Atli,
E'en after thine oaths sworn
To Gunnar full often;
Yea, oaths sworn of old time,
By the sun sloping southward,
By the high burg of Sigty,
By the fair bed of rest,
By the red ring of Ull!"

Now a host of men
Cast the high king alive
Into a close
Crept o'er within
With most foul worms,
Fulfilled of all venom,
Ready grave to dig
In his doughty heart.

Wrathful-hearted he smote
The harp with his hand,
Gunnar laid there alone;
And loud rang the strings.—
In such wise ever
Should hardy ring-scatterer
Keep gold from all folk
In the garth of his foemen.

Then Atli would wend
About his wide land,
On his steed brazen-shod,
Back from the murder.
Din there was in the garth,
All thronged with the horses;
High the weapon-song rose
From men come from the heath.

Out then went Gudrun,
'Gainst Atli returning,
With a cup gilded over,
To greet the land's ruler;
"Come, then, and take it,
King glad in thine hall,
From Gudrun's hands,
For the hell-farers groan not!"

Clashed the beakers of Atli,
Wine-laden on bench,
As in hall there a-gathered,
The Huns fell a-talking,
And the long-bearded eager ones
Entered therein,
From a murk den new-come,
From the murder of Gunnar.

Then hastened the sweet-faced
Delight of the shield-folk,
Bright in the fair hall,

Wine to bear to them:
The dreadful woman
Gave dainties withal
To the lords pale with fate,
Laid strange word upon Atli:

"The hearts of thy sons
Hast thou eaten, sword-dealer,
All bloody with death
And drenched with honey:
In most heavy mood
Brood o'er venison of men!
Drink rich draughts therewith,
Down the high benches send it!

"Never callest thou now
From henceforth to thy knee
Fair Erp or fair Eitil,
Bright-faced with the drink;
Never seest thou them now
Amidmost the seat,
Scattering the gold,
Or shafting of spears;
Manes trimming duly,
Or driving steeds forth!"

Din arose from the benches,
Dread song of men was there,
Noise 'mid the fair hangings,
As all Hun's children wept;
All saving Gudrun,
Who never gat greeting,
For her brethren bear-hardy,
For her sweet sons and bright,
The young ones, the simple
Once gotten with Atli.

. . . . .
. . . . .
. . . . .

The seed of gold
Sowed the swan-bright woman,
Rings of red gold
She gave to the house-carls;
Fate let she wax,
Let the bright gold flow forth,
In naught spared that woman
The store-houses' wealth.

Atli unaware
Was a-weary with drink;
No weapon had he,
No heeding of Gudrun—
Ah, the play would be better,
When in soft wise they twain
Would full often embrace
Before the great lords!

To the bed with sword-point
Blood gave she to drink
With a hand fain of death,
And she let the dogs loose:
Then in from the hall-door—
—Up waked the house-carls—
Hot brands she cast,
Gat revenge for her brethren.

To the flame gave she all
Who therein might be found;
Fell adown the old timbers,
Reeked all treasure-houses;
There the shield-mays were burnt,
Their lives' span brought to naught;
In the fierce fire sank down
All the stead of the Budlungs.

Wide told of is this—
Ne'er sithence in the world,
Thus fared bride clad in byrny

For her brothers' avenging;
For behold, this fair woman
To three kings of the people,
Hath brought very death
Or ever she died!

The Whetting of Gudrun

GUDRUN WENT down unto the sea whenas she had slain Atli, and she cast herself therein, for she was fain to end her life: but nowise might she drown. She drave over the firths to the land of King Jonakr, and he wedded her, and their sons were Sorli, and Erp, and Hamdir, and there was Swanhild, Sigurd's daughter, nourished: and she was given to Jormunrek the Mighty. Now Bikki was a man of his, and gave such counsel to Randver, the king's son, as that he should take her; and with that counsel were the young folk well content.

Then Bikki told the king, and the king let hang Randver, but bade Swanhild be trodden under horses' feet. But when Gudrun heard thereof, she spake to her sons—

> Words of strife heard I,
> Huger than any,
> Woeful words spoken,
> Sprung from all sorrow,
> When Gudrun fierce-hearted
> With the grimmest of words
> Whetted her sons
> Unto the slaying.

> "Why are ye sitting here?
> Why sleep ye life away?
> Why doth it grieve you nought?
> Glad words to speak,

Now when your sister—
Young of years was she—
Has Jormunrek trodden
With the treading of horses?—

"Black horses and white
In the highway of warriors:
Grey horses that know
The roads of the Goths.—

"Little like are ye grown
To that Gunnar of old days!
Nought are your hearts
As the heart of Hogni!
Well would ye seek
Vengeance to win
If your mood were in aught
As the mood of my brethren,
Or the hardy hearts
Of the Kings of the Huns!"

Then spake Hamdir,
The high-hearted—
"Little didst thou
Praise Hogni's doings,
When Sigurd woke
From out of sleep,
And the blue-white bed-gear
Upon thy bed
Grew red with man's blood—
With the blood of thy mate!

"Too baleful vengeance
Wroughtest thou for thy brethren
Most sore and evil
When thy sons thou slewedst,
Else all we together
On Jormunrek
Had wrought sore vengeance
For that our sister.

"Come, bring forth quickly
The Hun kings' bright gear,
Since thou hast urged us
Unto the sword-Thing!"

Laughing went Gudrun
To the bower of good gear,
Kings' crested helms
From chests she drew,
And wide-wrought byrnies
Bore to her sons:
Then on their horses
Load laid the heroes.

Then spake Hamdir,
The high-hearted—
"Never cometh again
His mother to see
The spear-god laid low
In the land of the Goths.
That one arvel mayst thou
For all of us drink,
For sister Swanhild,
And us thy sons."

Greeted Gudrun,
Giuki's daughter;
Sorrowing she went
In the forecourt to sit,
That she might tell,
With cheeks tear-furrowed,
Her weary wail
In many a wise.

"Three fires I knew,
To three husbands' houses
Have I been carried;
And better than all

Had been Sigurd alone,
He whom my brethren
Brought to his bane.

"Such sore grief as that
Methought never should be,
Yet more indeed
Was left for my torment
Then, when the great ones
Gave me to Atli.

"My fair bright boys
I bade unto speech,
Nor yet might I win
Weregild for my bale,
Ere I had hewn off
Those Niblungs' heads.

"To the sea-strand I went
With the Norns sorely wroth,
For I would thrust from me
The storm of their torment;
But the high billows
Would not drown, but bore me
Forth, till I stepped a-land
Longer to live.

"Then I went a-bed—
—Ah, better in the old days,
This was the third time!—
To a king of the people;
Offspring I brought forth,
Props of a fair house,
Props of a fair house,
Jonakr's fair sons.

"But around Swanhild
Bond-maidens sat,
Her, that of all mine
Most to my heart was;
Such was my Swanhild,

In my hall's midmost,
As is the sunbeam
Fair to behold.

"In gold I arrayed her,
And goodly raiment,
Or ever I gave her
To the folk of the Goths.
That was the hardest
Of my heavy woes,
When the bright hair,—
O the bright hair of Swanhild!—
In the mire was trodden
By the treading of horses.

"This was the sorest,
When my love, my Sigurd,
Reft of glory
In his bed gat ending:
But this the grimmest
When glittering worms
Tore their way
Through the heart of Gunnar.

"But this the keenest
When they cut to the quick
Of the hardy heart
Of the unfeared Hogni.
Of much of bale I mind me,
Of many griefs I mind me;
Why should I sit abiding
Yet more bale and more?

"Thy coal-black horse,
O Sigurd, bridle,
The swift on the highway!
O let him speed hither!

Here sitteth no longer
Son or daughter,

More good gifts
To give to Gudrun!

"Mindst thou not, Sigurd,
Of the speech betwixt us,
When on one bed
We both sat together,
O my great king—
That thou wouldst come to me
E'en from the hall of Hell,
I to thee from the fair earth?

"Pile high, O earls,
The oaken pile,
Let it be the highest
That ever queen had!
Let the fire burn swift,
My breast with woe laden,
And thaw all my heart,
Hard, heavy with sorrow!"

Now may all earls
Be bettered in mind,
May the grief of all maidens
Ever be minished,
For this tale of sorrow
So told to its ending.

The Lay of Hamdir

GREAT DEEDS of bale
In the garth began,
At the sad dawning
The tide of Elves' sorrow
When day is a-waxing
And man's grief awaketh,
And the sorrow of each one
The early day quickeneth.

Not now, not now,
Nor yesterday,
But long ago
Has that day worn by,
That ancientest time,
The first time to tell of,
Then, whenas Gudrun,
Born of Giuki,
Whetted her sons
To Swanhild's avenging.

"Your sister's name
Was naught but Swanhild,
Whom Jormunrek
With horses has trodden!—
White horses and black
On the war-beaten way,

Grey horses that go
On the roads of the Goths.

"All alone am I now
As in holt is the aspen;
As the fir-tree of boughs,
So of kin am I bare;
As bare of things longed for
As the willow of leaves
When the bough-breaking wind
The warm day endeth.

"Few, sad, are ye left,
O kings of my folk!
Yet alone living
Last shreds of my kin!

"Ah, naught are ye grown
As that Gunnar of old days;
Naught are your hearts
As the heart of Hogni!
Well would ye seek
Vengeance to win
If your hearts were in aught
As the hearts of my brethren!"

Then spake Hamdir
The high-hearted:
"Naught hadst thou to praise
The doings of Hogni,
When they woke up Sigurd
From out of slumber,
And in bed thou sat'st up
'Mid the banes-men's laughter.

"Then when thy bed-gear,
Blue-white, well woven
By art of craftsmen
All swam with thy king's blood;
Then Sigurd died,

O'er his dead corpse thou sattest,
Not heeding aught gladsome,
Since Gunnar so willed it.

"Great grief for Atli
Gatst thou by Erp's murder,
And the end of thine Eitil,
But worse grief for thyself.
Good to use sword
For the slaying of others
In such wise that its edge
Shall not turn on ourselves!"

Then well spake Sorli
From a heart full of wisdom:
"No words will I
Make with my mother,
Though both ye twain
Need words belike—
What askest thou, Gudrun,
To let thee go greeting?

"Weep for thy brethren,
Weep for thy sweet sons,
And thy nighest kinsfolk
Laid by the fight-side!
Yea, and thou Gudrun,
May'st greet for us twain
Sitting fey on our steeds
Doomed in far lands to die."

From the garth forth they went
With hearts full of fury,
Sorli and Hamdir,
The sons of Gudrun,
And they met on the way
The wise in all wiles:
"And thou little Erp,
What helping from thee?"

He of alien womb
Spake out in such wise:
"Good help for my kin,
Such as foot gives to foot,
Or flesh-covered hand
Gives unto hand!"

"What helping for foot
That help that foot giveth,
Or for flesh-covered hand
The helping of hand?"

Then spake Erp
Yet once again
Mock spake the prince
As he sat on his steed:
"Fool's deed to show
The way to a dastard!"
"Bold beyond measure,"
Quoth they, "is the base-born!"

Out from th sheath
Drew they the sheath-steel,
And the glaives' edges played
For the pleasure of hell;
By the third part they minished
The might that they had,
Their young kin they let lie
A-cold on the earth.

Then their fur-cloaks they shook
And bound fast their swords,
In webs goodly woven
Those great ones were clad;
Young they went o'er the fells
Where the dew was new-fallen
Swift, on steeds of the Huns,
Heavy vengeance to wreak.

Forth stretched the ways,

And an ill way they found,
Yea, their sister's son
Hanging slain upon tree—
Wolf-trees by the wind made cold
At the town's westward
Loud with cranes' clatter—
Ill abiding there long!

Din in the king's hall
Of men merry with drink,
And none might hearken
The horses' tramping
Or ever the warders
Their great horn winded.

Then men went forth
To Jormunrek
To tell of the heeding
Of men under helm:
"Give ye good counsel!
Great ones are come hither,
For the wrong of men mighty
Was the may to death trodden."

Loud Jormunrek laughed,
And laid hand to his beard,
Nor bade bring his byrny,
But with the wine fighting,
Shook his red locks,
On his white shield sat staring,
And in his hand
Swung the gold cup on high.

"Sweet sight for me
Those twain to set eyes on,
Sorli and Hamdir,
Here in my hall!
Then with bowstrings
Would I bind them,
And hang the good Giukings

Aloft on the gallows!"

.   .   .   .   .

.   .   .   .   .

.   .   .   .   .

Then spake Hrothglod
From off the high steps,
Spake the slim-fingered
Unto her son,—
—For a threat was cast forth
Of what ne'er should fall—
"Shall two men alone
Two hundred Gothfolk
Bind or bear down
In the midst of their burg?"

.   .   .   .   .

.   .   .   .   .

Strife and din in the hall,
Cups smitten asunder
Men lay low in blood
From the breasts of Goths flowing.

Then spake Hamdir,
The high-hearted:
"Thou cravedst, O king,
For the coming of us,
The sons of one mother,
Amidmost thine hall—
Look on these hands of thine,
Look on these feet of thine,
Cast by us, Jormunrek,
On to the flame!"

Then cried aloud
The high Gods' kinsman,
Bold under byrny,—
Roared he as bears roar;
"Stones to the stout ones
That the spears bite not,

Nor the edges of steel,
These sons of Jonakr!"

. . . . .

. . . . .

Quoth Sorli.

"Bale, brother, wroughtst thou
By that bag's opening,
Oft from that bag
Rede of bale cometh!
Heart hast thou, Hamdir,
If thou hadst heart's wisdom
Great lack in a man
Who lacks wisdom and lore!"

Hamdir said.

"Yea, off were the head
If Erp were alive yet,
Our brother the bold
Whom we slew by the way;
The far-famed through the world.—
Ah, the fates drave me on,
And the man war made holy,
There must I slay!"

Sorli said.

"Unmeet we should do
As the doings of wolves are,
Raising wrong each 'gainst other
As the dogs of the Norns,
The greedy ones nourished
In waste steads of the world.

In strong wise have we fought,
On Goths' corpses we stand,
Beat down by our edges,
E'en as ernes on the bough.
Great fame our might winneth,

Die we now, or to-morrow,—
No man lives till eve
Whom the fates doom at morning."
At the hall's gable-end
Fell Sorli to earth,
But Hamdir lay low
At the back of the houses.

Now this is called the Ancient Lay of Hamdir.

The Lament of Oddrun

THERE WAS a king hight Heidrik, and his daughter was called Borgny, and the name of her lover was Vilmund. Now she might nowise be made lighter of a child she travailed with, before Oddrun, Atli's sister, came to her,—she who had been the love of Gunnar, Giuki's son. But of their speech together has this been sung:

> I have heard tell
> In ancient tales
> How a may there came
> To Morna-land,
> Because no man
> On mould abiding
> For Heidrik's daughter
> Might win healing.

> All that heard Oddrun,
> Atli's sister,
> How that the damsel
> Had heavy sickness,
> So she led from stall
> Her bridled steed,
> And on the swart one
> Laid the saddle.

> She made her horse wend
> O'er smooth ways of earth,

Until to a high-built
Hall she came;
Then the saddle she had
From the hungry horse,
And her ways wended
In along the wide hall,
And this word first
Spake forth therewith:

"What is most famed,
Afield in Hunland,
Or what may be
Blithest in Hunland?"

Quoth the handmaid.

"Here lieth Borgny,
Borne down by trouble,
Thy sweet friend, O Oddrun,
See to her helping!"

Oddrun said.

"Who of the lords
Hath laid this grief on her,
Why is the anguish
Of Borgny so weary?"

The handmaid said.

"He is hight Vilmund,
Friend of hawk-bearers,
He wrapped the damsel
In the warm bed-gear
Five winters long
Without her father's wotting."

No more than this
They spake methinks;
Kind sat she down

By the damsel's knee;
Mightily sang Oddrun,
Eagerly sang Oddrun,
Sharp piercing songs
By Borgny's side:

Till a maid and a boy
Might tread on the world's ways,
Blithe babes and sweet
Of Hogni's bane:
Then the damsel forewearied
The word took up,
The first word of all
That had won from her:

"So may help thee
All helpful things,
Fey and Freyia,
And all the fair Gods,
As thou hast thrust
This torment from me!"

Oddrun said.

"Yet no heart had I
For thy helping,
Since never wert thou
Worthy of helping,
But my word I held to,
That of old was spoken
When the high lords
Dealt out the heritage,
That every soul
I would ever help."

Borgny said.

"Right mad art thou, Oddrun,
And reft of thy wits,
Whereas thou speakest

Hard words to me
Thy fellow ever
Upon the earth
As of brothers twain,
We had been born."

Oddrun said.

"Well I mind me yet,
What thou saidst that evening,
Whenas I bore forth
Fair drink for Gunnar;
Such a thing, saidst thou,
Should fall out never,
For any may
Save for me alone."

Mind had the damsel
Of the weary day
Whenas the high lords
Dealt out the heritage,
And she sat her down,
The sorrowful woman,
To tell of the bale,
And the heavy trouble.

"Nourished was I
In the hall of kings—
Most folk were glad—
'Mid the council of great ones:
In fair life lived I,
And the wealth of my father
For five winters only,
While yet he had life.

"Such were the last words
That ever he spake,
The king forewearied,
Ere his ways he went;
For he bade folk give me

The gold red-gleaming,
And give me in Southlands
To the son of Grimhild.

"But Brynhild he bade
To the helm to betake her,
And said that Death-chooser
She should become;
And that no better
Might ever be born
Into the world,
If fate would not spoil it.

"Brynhild in bower
Sewed at her broidery,
Folk she had
And fair lands about her;
Earth lay a-sleeping,
Slept the heavens aloft
When Fafnir's-bane
The burg first saw.

"Then was war waged
With the Welsh-wrought sword
And the burg all broken
That Brynhild owned;
Nor wore long space,
E'en as well might be,
Ere all those wiles
Full well she knew.

"Hard and dreadful
Was the vengeance she drew down,
So that all we
Have woe enow.

Through all lands of the world
Shall that story fare forth
How she did her to death
For the death of Sigurd.

"But therewithal Gunnar
The gold-scatterer
Did I fall to loving
And she should have loved him.
Rings of red gold
Would they give to Atli,
Would give to my brother
Things goodly and great.

"Yea, fifteen steads
Would they give for me,
And the load of Grani
To have as a gift;
But then spake Atli,
That such was his will,
Never gift to take
From the sons of Giuki.

"But we in nowise
Might love withstand,
And mine head must I lay
On my love, the ring-breaker;
And many there were
Among my kin,
Who said that they
Had seen us together.

"Then Atli said
That I surely never
Would fall to crime
Or shameful folly:
But now let no one
For any other,
That shame deny
Where love has dealing.

"For Atli sent
His serving-folk
Wide through the murkwood
Proof to win of me,

And thither they came
Where they ne'er should have come,
Where one bed we twain
Had dight betwixt us.

"To those men had we given
Rings of red gold,
Naught to tell
Thereof to Atli,
But straight they hastened
Home to the house,
And all the tale
To Atli told.

"Whereas from Gudrun
Well they hid it,
Though better by half
Had she have known it.

. . . . .
. . . . .

"Din was there to hear
Or the hoofs gold-shod,
When into the garth
Rode the sons of Giuki.

"There from Hogni
The heart they cut,
But into the worm-close
Cast the other.
There the king, the wise-hearted,
Swept his harp-strings,
For the mighty king
Had ever mind
That I to his helping
Soon should come.

"But now was I gone
Yet once again
Unto Geirmund,

Good feast to make;
Yet had I hearing,
E'en out from Hlesey,
How of sore trouble
The harp-strings sang.

"So I bade the bondmaids
Be ready swiftly,
For I listed to save
The life of the king,
And we let our ship
Swim over the sound,
Till Atli's dwelling
We saw all clearly.

Then came the wretch
Crawling out,
E'en Atli's mother,
All sorrow upon her!
A grave gat her sting
In the heart of Gunnar,
So that no helping
Was left for my hero.

"O gold-clad woman,
Full oft I wonder
How I my life
Still hold thereafter,
For methought I loved
That light in battle,
The swift with the sword,
As my very self.

"Thou hast sat and hearkened
As I have told thee
Of many an ill-fate,
Mine and theirs—
Each man liveth
E'en as he may live—
Now hath gone forth
The greeting of Oddrun."

Glossary

Aesir a race of gods

Alf son of Hjalprek, king of Denmark; second husband of Hjordis

Alswid son of Heimir and Bekkhild

Andvari a dwarf

Asgarth the city of the Aesir

Aslaug daughter of Brynhild and Sigurd

Asyniur goddesses

Atli Brynhild's brother; Gudrun's second husband

Bekkhild sister of Brynhild and Atli; wife of Heimir

Bikki Jormunrek's counselor

Borghild Sigmund's first wife; mother of Helgi

Brynhild sister of Atli and Bekkhild; wife of Gunnar; mother of Aslaug by Sigurd

Budli father of Brynhild, Atli, Bekkhild, and Oddrun

Disir guardian spirits

Erp son of Jonakr and Gudrun; brother of Hamdir and Sorli

Eylimi father of Hjordis and Grifir

Fafnir eldest son of Hreidmar; brother of Otter and Regin

Freyia a goddess, part Vanir and part Aesir

Giuki husband of Grimhild; father of Gunnar, Hogni, Guttorm, and Gudrun

Glaumvor Gunnar's second wife

Gram the sword of Sigmund and Sigurd

Grani Sigurd's horse descended from Sleipnir

Grifir (Gripir) son of Eylimi and brother of Hjordis

Grimhild wife of Giuki

Gudrun daughter of Giuki; sister of Gunnar, Hogni, and Guttorm; wife of (1) Sigurd, (2) Atli, and (3) Jonakr

Gunnar son of Giuki; brother of Hogni, Guttorm, and Gudrun; husband of (1) Brynhild and (2) Glaumvor

Guttorm son of Giuki; brother of Gunnar, Hogni, and Gudrun

Hamdir son of Jonakr and Gudrun; brother of Sorli and Erp

Heimir husband of Bekkhild; father of Alswid; foster-father of Brynhild

Helgi son of Sigmund and Borghild; husband of Sigrun

Hindfell a mountain in the land of the Franks

Hjalprek king of Denmark; father of Alf

Hjordis daughter of Eylimi; second wife of Sigmund; mother of Sigurd

Hlymdale the city of Heimir

Hnikar a warrior who seeks to travel with Sigurd

Hoenir one of the Aesir

Hogni son of Giuki; brother of Gunnar, Guttorm, and

Gudrun; husband of Kostbera

Hogni father of Sigrun

Hreidmar father of Fafnir, Otter, and Regin

Hunding a king defeated by Helgi; father of Lyngi

Jonakr third husband of Gudrun; father of Hamdir, Sorli, and Erp

Jormunrek husband of Swanhild; father of Randver

Kostbera wife of Hogni, son of Giuki

Ljod daughter of Hrimnir the giant; wife of V o l s u n g; mother of Sigmund and Signy

Loki one of the Aesir

Lyngi son of Hunding

Nibelung son of Hogni; grandson of Giuki

Norns goddesses of destiny

Oddrun sister of Atli, Brynhild, and Bekkhild

Odin chief of the Aesir

Otter middle son of Hreidmar; brother of Fafnir and Regin

Ragna rök the doom of the gods

Ran a sea goddess

Randver son of Jormunrek; lover of Swanhild

Regin youngest son of Hreidmar; brother of Fafnir and Otter

Rerir son of Sigi

Siggeir king of the Goths; husband of Signy

Sigi son of Odin

Sigmund son of Volsung and Ljod; brother of Signy; husband of (1) Borghild and

(2) Hjordis; father of Sinfjotli, Helgi, and Sigurd

Sigmund son of Sigurd and Gudrun

Signy daughter of Volsung and Ljod; sister of the elder Sigmund; wife of Siggeir; mother of Sinfjotli

Sigrun daughter of Hogni (not Giuki's son); wife of Helgi; sister of Dag

Sigurd son of Sigmund and Hjordis; husband of Gudrun; father of Sigmund, Swanhild, and Aslaug (by Brynhild)

Sinfjotli son of Sigmund and Signy; half brother to Helgi and Sigurd

Sleipnir horse of Odin

Sorli son of Jonakr and Gudrun; brother of Hamdir and Erp

Surt a fire giant who enkindles the universe at the twilight of the gods

Swanhild daughter of Sigurd and Gudrun; wife of Jormunrek; half sister of Hamdir, Sorli, and Erp

Vanir a race of gods once rivals of but later reconciled to the Aesir

Vingi Atli's messenger

Volsung son of Rerir; husband of Ljod; father of Sigmund and Signy

Valkyrie one of the warriormaids who after battle gathers the dead heroes to join Odin at Walhall

Walhall the hall of heroes at Asgarth

Wolf in holy places an outlaw

Reading List

The Collected Works of Henrik Ibsen. In English, edited by William Archer. New York, C. Scribner's Sons, 1909–22.

The Collected Works of William Morris. With Introductions by his daughter, May Morris. Longmans Green and Co., London, New York, Bombay, Calcutta, 1910–15.

Newman, Ernest, *The Life of Richard Wagner*. New York, Alfred A. Knopf, 1942–46.

The Nibelungenlied. Translated into English prose by Margaret Armour. New York, E. P. Dutton and Co., 1939.

The Poetic Edda. Translated from the Icelandic by Henry Adams Bellows. New York, The American-Scandinavian Foundation, 1923.

The Prose Edda, Snorri Sturluson. Translated from the Icelandic by Arthur Gilchrist Brodeur. New York, The American-Scandinavian Foundation, 1916.

Richard Wagner's Prose Works. Translated by William Ashton Ellis. London, K. Paul, Trench, Trübner and Co., 1892–99.

Shaw, G. Bernard, *The Perfect Wagnerite*. New York, Brentano's, 1911.

Wagner, Richard, *The Ring of the Nibelung*. Translated into English by Margaret Armour. Garden City, Garden City Publishing Co., 1939.